The Montana Council of Teachers of Mathematics

The Systemic Initiative for Montana Mathematics and Science

INTEGRATED MATHEMATICS

A MODELING APPROACH USING TECHNOLOGY

TEACHER'S EDITION

Volume 3

SIMON & SCHUSTER CUSTOM PUBLISHING

SIMMS PROJECT CO-DIRECTORS

Johnny W. Lott • Maurice Burke

MATERIALS DEVELOPMENT COMMITTEE

Dean Preble • Terry Souhrada

ASSESSMENT COMMITTEE

James Hirstein • Sharon Walen

PROFESSIONAL DEVELOPMENT COMMITTEE

Glenn Allinger • Michael Lundin

TECHNICAL EDITOR

Peter Fong

SIMMS CURRICULUM REVIEWERS

Participants of the SIMMS Teacher Institutes and Staff

This material is based upon work supported by the National Science Foundation under Cooperative Agreement No. OSR 9150055. Any opinions, findings, conclusions or recommendations expressed in this material are those of the author(s) and do not necessarily reflect the views of the National Science Foundation.

Printed in the United States of America.

10 9 8 7 6 5 4 3 2

BA 98273

ISBN 0–536–59534–8

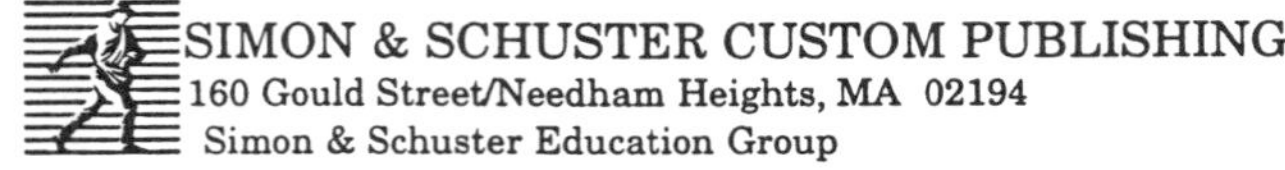

SIMON & SCHUSTER CUSTOM PUBLISHING
160 Gould Street/Needham Heights, MA 02194
Simon & Schuster Education Group

About SIMMS Integrated Mathematics

The Need for Change

In recent years, many voices have called for the reform of mathematics education in the United States. Teachers, scholars, and administrators alike have pointed out the symptoms of a flawed system. From the ninth grade onwards, for example, about half of the students in this country's mathematical pipeline are lost each year (National Research Council, 1990, p. 36). Attempts to identify the root causes of this decline have targeted not only the methods used to instruct and assess our students, but the nature of the mathematics they learn and the manner in which they are expected to learn. In its *Curriculum and Evaluation Standards for School Mathematics*, the National Council of Teachers of Mathematics addressed the problem in these terms:

> Deciding on the content of school mathematics is the initial step in the necessary change process. . . .
>
> We now challenge educators to integrate mathematics topics across courses so that students can view major mathematical ideas from more than one perspective and bring interrelated ideas to bear on new topics or problems. . . .
>
> We favor . . . a truly integrated curricular organization in all grades to permit students to develop mathematical power more readily and to allow the necessary flexibility over time to incorporate the content of these standards. (p. 251–52)

Some Methods for Change

The Systemic Initiative for Montana Mathematics and Science (SIMMS) was a five-year, cooperative initiative of the state of Montana and the National Science Foundation. Funded through the Montana Council of Teachers of Mathematics, the SIMMS Project included the following among its major objectives:

- the redesign of the 9–12 mathematics curriculum using an integrated interdisciplinary approach for *all* students.
- the incorporation of the use of technology in all facets and at all levels of mathematics and science.
- the development of curriculum and assessment materials for grades 9–16.

The SIMMS Curriculum

An integrated mathematics program "consists of topics chosen from a wide variety of mathematical fields. . . [It] emphasizes the relationships among topics within mathematics as well as between mathematics and other disciplines" (Beal, et al., 1992; Lott, 1991). In order to create innovative, integrated, and accessible materials, the SIMMS curriculum was written, revised, and reviewed by secondary teachers of mathematics and science. SIMMS materials encourage participation by women and members of ethnic minorities, and are intended for use by heterogeneous groupings of students. They are designed to replace all currently offered secondary mathematics courses, with the possible exception of Advanced Placement Calculus, and build on middle-school reform initiatives, such as the Six Through Eight Mathematics (STEM) Project.

SIMMS curricular materials are partitioned into six levels. All students should take at least the first two levels. In the third and fourth years, SIMMS offers a choice of options, depending on student interests and goals. A flow chart of the curriculum appears in Figure 1.

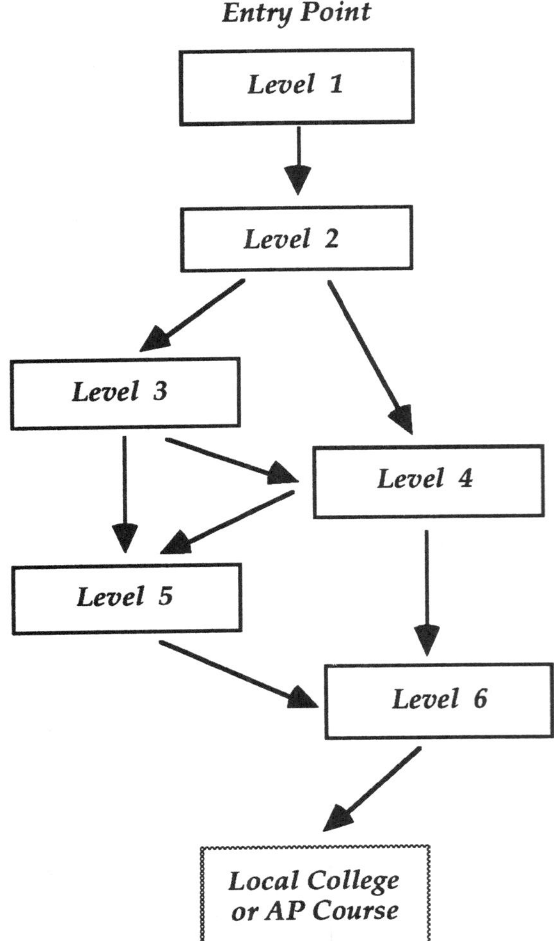

Figure 1: SIMMS course sequence

Each year-long level contains 14–16 modules. Some must be presented in sequence, while others may be studied in any order. Modules are further divided into several activities, typically including an exploration, a discussion, a set of homework assignments, and a research project.

Assessment materials—including alternative assessments that emphasize writing and logical argument—are an integral part of the curriculum. Suggested assessment items for use with a standard rubric are identified in all teacher editions. Each module also contains an open-ended, often project-oriented summary assessment, as well as a more traditional assessment (for use at the teacher's discretion).

Level 1: a first-year course for ninth graders (or possibly eighth graders)

Level 1 concentrates on the knowledge and understanding that students need to become mathematically literate citizens, while providing the necessary foundation for those who wish to pursue careers involving mathematics and science. Contexts for the presentation of mathematics include the properties of reflected light, population growth, the AIDS epidemic, and the manufacture of cardboard containers. Mathematical content includes data collection, presentation, and interpretation; introductions to linear, exponential, and step equations; and three-dimensional geometry, including surface area and volume.

Level 2: a second-year course for either ninth or tenth graders

Level 2 continues to build on the mathematics that students need to become mathematically literate citizens. While retaining an emphasis on the presentation and interpretation of data, Level 2 introduces trigonometric ratios and matrices, while also encouraging the development of algebraic skills. Contexts include pyramid construction, small business inventory, genetics, and the allotment of seats in the U.S. House of Representatives.

Levels 3 and 4: options for students in their third year in SIMMS

Both of these levels build on the mathematics content in Level 2 and provide an opportunity for students to expand their mathematical understanding. While most students planning careers in mathematics and science will choose Level 4, Level 3 also provides insight into some topics typically studied by mathematics and science majors.

Contexts in Level 4 include launching a new business, historic rainfall patterns, topography, and scheduling. The mathematical content includes rational, logarithmic, and circular functions, proofs, and combinatorics.

In Level 3, module contexts include nutrition, surveying, and quality control. Mathematical topics include linear programming, polynomial functions, and curve fitting.

Levels 5 and 6: options for students in their fourth year in SIMMS

Level 6 materials continue the presentation of mathematics through applied contexts while embracing a broader mathematical perspective. For example, Level 6 modules explore operations on functions, instantaneous rates of change, complex numbers, and parametric equations.

Level 5 focuses more specifically on applications from business and the social sciences, including statistics testing, logic circuits, and game theory.

More About Level 2

"Marvelous Matrices" introduces matrix operations in the context of business inventories. "When to Deviate from a Mean Task" and "And the Survey Says . . ." focus on statistics and sampling, respectively. "A New Angle on an Old Pyramid," "There's No Place Like Home," and "Crazy Cartoons" have primarily geometric themes. "Traditional Design" also explores some geometric topics—this time from the perspective of American Indian star quilts. "Who Gets What and Why?" examines the mathematics of apportionment to the U.S. House of Representatives. Other modules explore linear programming, multistage probability, models of exponential decay, curve fitting, and the limits of sequences and series. Some teachers may wish to schedule the genetics module—"What Are My Child's Chances?"—in coordination with a biology class.

The Teacher Edition

To facilitate use of the curriculum, the teacher edition contains these features:

Overview /Objectives/Prerequisites

Each module begins with a brief overview of its contents. This overview is followed by a list of teaching objectives and a list of prerequisite skills and knowledge.

Time Line/Materials &Technology Required

A time line provides a rough estimate of the classroom periods required to complete each module. The materials required for the entire module are listed by activity. The technology required to complete the module appears in a similar list.

Assignment Problems/Assessment Items/Flashbacks

Assignment problems appear at the end of each activity. These problems are separated into two sections by a series of asterisks. The problems in the first section cover all the essential elements in the activity. The second section provides optional problems for extra practice or additional homework.

Specific assignment problems recommended for assessment are preceded by a single asterisk in the teacher edition. Each module also contains a Summary Assessment in the student edition and a Module Assessment in the teacher edition, for use at the teacher's discretion. In general, Summary Assessments offer more open-ended questions, while Module Assessments take a more traditional approach.

To review prerequisite skills, each module includes brief problem sets called "Flashbacks." Like the Module Assessment, they are designed for use at the teacher's discretion.

Technology in the Classroom

The SIMMS curriculum requires the appropriate use of technology. Individual graphing calculators should be available to all students. Classroom technology should have the functionality and memory to run a word processing program, a statistics package, a graphing package, a symbolic manipulator, a spreadsheet program, and a geometric drawing utility. In addition, SIMMS students should have access to a telephone modem, as well as a science interface device that allows for electronic data collection from classroom experiments.

In the student edition, references to technology provide as much flexibility as possible to the teacher. In the teacher edition, sample responses refer to specific pieces of technology, where applicable.

Professional Development

A program of professional development is recommended for all teachers planning to use the SIMMS curriculum. SIMMS materials encourage the use of cooperative learning, consider mathematical topics in a different order than in a traditional curriculum, and teach some mathematical topics not previously encountered at the high-school level. Teachers must also learn to use alternative assessments, to integrate writing and communication into the mathematics curriculum, and to help students incorporate technology in their own investigations of mathematical ideas.

Approximately 100 classroom teachers and 15 university professors are available to present inservice workshops for interested school districts. Please contact Simon & Schuster Custom Publishing for more information.

Project Assessment to Date

Assessment instruments have been administered in selected SIMMS classes using Levels 1–6. On both the non-technology-based PSAT and a test of problem-solving skills allowing use of technology, the results are very encouraging. When compared with the control group, students in SIMMS classes did as well as students in a traditional program on a test of general mathematical knowledge. On more open-ended questions, SIMMS students showed superior skills in problem-solving and communicating mathematical ideas, used a wider variety of problem-solving strategies, and used appropriate technology.

References

Beal, J., D. Dolan, J. Lott, and J. Smith. *Integrated Mathematics: Definitions, Issues, and Implications; Report and Executive Summary.* ERIC Clearinghouse for Science, Mathematics, and Environmental Education. The Ohio State University, Columbus, OH: ED 347071, January 1990, 115 pp.

Lott, J., and A. Reeves. "The Integrated Mathematics Project," *Mathematics Teacher* 84 (April 1991): 334–35.

National Council of Teachers of Mathematics (NCTM). *Curriculum and Evaluation Standards for School Mathematics.* Reston, VA: NCTM, 1989.

National Research Council. *A Challenge of Numbers: People in the Mathematical Sciences.* Washington, DC: National Academy Press, 1990.

The SIMMS Project. *Monograph 1: Philosophies.* Missoula, MT: The Montana Council of Teachers of Mathematics, 1993.

Contents

And the Survey Says . . .

How can television newscasters predict the next president of the United States long before the votes are counted? In this module, you explore some of the basics of sampling and surveys.

Staci Auck • Kyle Boyce • Tom Teegarden

Teacher Edition
And the Survey Says . . .

Overview

In this module, students explore methods of sampling. They examine potential sources of bias and experiment with different types of sampling. Histograms are used to represent data and to predict characteristics of a population. Confidence statements and margins of error are introduced as methods for interpreting the results of a survey.

Objectives

In this module, students will:

- use a variety of sampling techniques
- predict the characteristics of a population based on samples
- explore the role that biases play in sampling
- use histograms to estimate probabilities and make predictions
- investigate how sample size affects a survey's reliability
- explore confidence statements and margins of error.

Prerequisites

For this module, students should know:

- how to calculate mean and standard deviation
- how to create frequency tables
- how to construct histograms.

Time Line

Activity	1	2	3	4	Summary Assessment	Total
Days	1	2	3	2	2	10

Materials Required

Materials	Activity				
	1	2	3	4	Summary Assessment
graph paper		X	X		
paper bags	X		X		
dry beans	X		X		
template of town map		X			

Teacher Note

A blackline master of the template appears at the end of this teacher edition.

Technology

Software	Activity				
	1	2	3	4	Summary Assessment
statistics package			X	X	X
spreadsheet		X	X	X	X
graphing utility				X	
random number generator		X			
programmable calculator (optional)			X	X	X

And the Survey Says . . .

Introduction

You may wish to ask students to discuss some recent opinion polls.

Activity 1

Using a population of two different kinds of beans, students explore the effects of biased sampling methods on attempts to characterize a population. **Note:** This activity introduces students to some terms used throughout the module: *population*, *parameter*, *sample*, *statistic*, *census*, and *bias*.

Materials List

- two varieties of dry beans that are significantly different in size (about 150 beans per group)
- paper bags or other opaque containers (one per group)

Teacher Note

Each population should consist of a total of about 150 beans of two different sizes—for example, kidney beans and lentils. (The actual proportion of the smaller beans to larger beans is unimportant.)

Exploration

a. When students take samples by the handful, the size difference in the two kinds of beans creates a bias in favor of the larger beans.

b. The following sample data was collected using a population of 30% kidney beans and 70% lentils.

Sample	Kidney Beans	Lentils
1	77%	23%
2	60%	40%
3	57%	43%
4	38%	63%
5	64%	36%
Mean	59%	41%

c. Answers will vary. Students may use the mean percentages from their five samples to predict the population percentages. (See sample data given in Part **b**.)

d. This actual proportions of beans in the population may differ considerably from student predictions.

Discussion

a.
1. The percentages of each type of bean determined in the census are parameters.
2. The percentages of each type of bean in a sample (as well as the means of these percentages) are statistics.

b. Sample response: The data collected by sampling predicted a higher percentage of the larger beans and a lower percentage of the smaller beans than are actually in the population.

c. The sampling method—in combination with the difference in the size of the beans—creates bias. When sampling by the handful, larger beans have a better chance of being selected since smaller ones tend to slip through the fingers.

d. Students should suggest sampling techniques that give each bean the same chance of being selected. For example, using a cup to select the sample may help to reduce the bias in favor of the larger beans.

e. Real-life surveys often ignore segments of the population through biased sampling. For example, telephone surveys eliminate anyone who does not own a phone. If conducted during normal business hours, they may also eliminate people who do not work at home. Other polls solicit voluntary responses and therefore count only those people with strong opinions. Since many magazines target specific audiences, their polls are limited to a select readership. Polls taken on downtown streets or in shopping malls exclude large segments of the general population. The wording of questions, especially regarding sensitive topics, may also bias a survey.

f. Because of the descriptive adjectives used to praise the eagle and belittle the bison, this survey question is biased in favor of the eagle. To reduce bias, the question may be rephrased as follows: "Would you prefer the eagle or the bison as the school mascot, or do you have no opinion?"

Assignment

1.1 Answers will vary. Such surveys do not provide random samples for several reason. Many dial-in surveys charge a small fee for the call, which creates bias against those unwilling to pay. Often, only those people who have strong opinions about the topic will call. The most significant bias, of course, is against people who are not watching the program.

1.2 Responses may vary. This type of survey also does not give everyone in the population an equal chance to be in the sample. The polling method excludes those who do not visit shopping malls. Of those who are questioned, several members of the same household might answer affirmatively, although each individual does not own a separate VCR.

***1.3**

a. The population is the 2380 Washington High School students.

b. Students should describe methods that survey every student in the school population. Sample response: Send a person to poll every first-period class in the school. Check records for any students without a first-period class and find them in the next available class.

c. Answers will vary. Three sample responses are listed below.

1. Choose the first person who walks into the cafeteria at lunch time and every 10th person after that.
2. Select all the sophomores in one homeroom class.
3. Write a computer program to generate random numbers that correspond with student ID numbers. Sample those students whose ID numbers match the computer-generated numbers.

d. The following list describes some advantages and disadvantages to the sample responses in Part **c**.

1. This type of sample is easy to administer. However, not all students may eat lunch in the cafeteria. The students who don't will be excluded from the sample.
2. This type of sample is also easy to administer. But since all students other than sophomores are excluded, as well as all other students not in that homeroom, the sample is extremely biased.
3. Since every student has an equal chance of being selected, this method produces a random sample. It may take some time and effort, however, to write a computer program that will generate appropriate numbers.

1.4 **a.** In 1936, many people did not own a car or a telephone. A significant portion of the voting population was therefore excluded from the survey.

b. The pollsters should have designed a survey that gave every registered voter an equal chance of being selected. (**Note:** George Gallup did an accurate poll for this election, and his career as a pollster blossomed.)

1.5 Sample response: In a survey on providing housing for the homeless, the following question would be biased in favor of a "yes" response: "If some friends of yours suddenly became homeless, would you want them to be provided with housing?" By including the clause about friends, the question creates bias. Most people would not want to have friends in such a desperate situation. If the question was rewritten as follows—"Would you vote for a bond issue to provide housing for the homeless?"—the number of affirmative answers might change dramatically.

* * * * *

1.6 **a.** Sample response: No. Jordan's survey does not necessarily provide a representative sample of the population, since it contains only his classmates and friends. **Note:** You may wish to point out that although a random sample also may not necessarily provide a representative sample of a population, the manner in which it was selected is unbiased.

b. Jordan's survey question appears to be relatively free of bias. Some students may argue, however, that the question is biased towards rock and roll, since this category is listed first.

Since music preferences tend to be similar among friends, his survey technique introduces a bias against the preferences of other students in the school.

c. To eliminate bias in the sampling method, students may suggest that Jordan randomly select 50 people from a list of the entire school population.

1.7 **a.** Sample response: Because of her use of the word *confined*, Susanne appears to favor the proposal.

b. Sample response: "Do you want to have open campus for the lunch period even though it would lengthen the school day by 15 minutes?"

c. Sample response: "Are you in favor of or against an open campus lunch, or do you have no opinion?"

* * * * * * * * * *

Research Project

a. Student summaries should include a description of the population, the sample size, and the sampling technique, as well as a discussion of potential bias in the survey.

b. Students may need some guidance on possible topics and on the format of their presentations. You may wish to consult with a history teacher for suggestions.

Activity 2

This activity focuses on different types of sampling techniques, including stratified sampling and systematic sampling.

Materials List

- template of town map (one per student; a blackline master appears at the end of this teacher edition)

Technology

- statistics package
- random number generator

Exploration

The exploration provides hands-on activities that allow students to examine different sampling techniques. **Note:** Students sample from a map of a town divided into districts. This is a much simplified version of an actual district map. Typical voting districts or precincts often have irregular boundaries (and populations that are not multiples of 100).

a. Allowing students to select their own samples may illustrate the need for sampling techniques that eliminate unintentional biases. Students often choose one small, one large, and two medium-sized districts. This creates bias, since after one small district is chosen, for example, the other small districts do not have an equal chance of being selected in the sample. Students may also tend to choose only rectangular districts, which creates bias against those with other shapes.

1. The populations of individual districts vary from 100 to 600 people.
2. Answers will vary. Many students will calculate the mean population of the four districts in their sample. The actual mean is 207.5.

3. Estimates will vary. Students may multiply the mean number of people per district by the total number of districts (40), multiply the number of people in their four samples by 10, or devise other methods.

b. The actual population of the town is 8300.

c. Student results will vary. A random sample of districts 25, 40, 39, and 32 results in the following mean population per district:

$$\frac{200+300+100+200}{4}=200$$

This corresponds with a population estimate of $200 \bullet 40 = 8000$.

d. Answers will vary. Some students may group districts by size and select one at random from each subgroup. Others may group districts by location or district number. For example, the two highways divide the town into four regions. Each region could be considered a stratum.

Using this method, the following four districts might be selected: 4, 15, 21, and 37. For this sample, the mean population per district is:

$$\frac{300+200+300+400}{4}=300$$

This corresponds with a population estimate of $300 \bullet 40 = 12{,}000$

e. 1. Sample response: Starting with region 5, select every 10th region after that. The sample contain regions 5, 15, 25, and 35.

2. The mean population per district for the sample described in Step **1** is:

$$\frac{200+200+200+200}{4}=200$$

This corresponds with a population estimate of $200 \bullet 40 = 8000$.

Discussion

a. Since different samples can be selected using the same method, identical sampling techniques do not necessarily produce identical results. The class data should illustrate this point.

b. An intuitive sampling method will not guarantee that every district has the same chance of being selected.

Depending on how strata are determined or on how samples are selected from each stratum, bias may or may not appear in a stratified sampling method.

A systematic sampling method might introduce bias through the selection of the starting point and the value of *n*.

Since each district has the same chance of inclusion in a simple random sample, this method has no apparent bias.

c. The sampling method based on intuition allows the most bias. Simple random sampling has the least potential for bias because every district has an equal chance of being selected.

Assignment

2.1

a. This method does not produce a simple random sample because everyone in the school may not eat in the cafeteria and because it selects only those who arrive early.

b. This method produces a simple random sample because every student has an equal chance of selection.

c. This method produces a simple random sample of boys and a simple random sample of girls, but not a simple random sample of students, since selections depend on gender. This is an example of stratified sampling by gender.

d. This method produces a simple random sample because every student has an equal chance of selection.

e. This method does not produce a simple random sample because it is biased against students who do not attend the pep assembly. This is an example of systematic sampling.

f. This method produces a simple random sample only if student ID numbers are randomly issued (and some ID numbers end with 0).

2.2 Since it creates subgroups by gender, the method described in Part **c** represents stratified sampling. Because it selects every *n*th unit of the population, starting with the first student, the method described in Part **e** represents systematic sampling

***2.3**

a. 1. Sample response: Write the names of all students on identical slips of paper, put the slips into a bin, mix them thoroughly, and draw out 20 slips.

2. Sample response: Select five names at random from each of the four classes: seniors, juniors, sophomores, and freshmen.

3. Sample response: Select the first person who walks into the next school-wide assembly and every 10th person after that, until you have selected 20 people.

b. The following answers correspond with the sample responses given in Part **a**.

1. Since this is a simple random sample, where each name has the same chance of being selected in the sample, there is little potential for bias.

2. Some bias may occur in the stratified approach since each student is not selected independently. The proportions of students from each class in the sample may not reflect their proportions in the population. **Note:** When the sample sizes are proportional to the sizes of the strata, this type of stratified sampling is known as *proportional sampling*.

c. This method selects from only those students who attend the assembly. (Also, if fewer than 200 students attend, it will not provide the desired sample size.)

2.4 Answers will vary. Students should not feel compelled to use simple random samples. Depending on the purposes of the survey, a different method—such as stratified sampling—could eliminate other biases, even though it does not produce a simple random sample. In a survey of dating preferences, for example, it might be appropriate to guarantee equal participation by males and females and by each class.

2.5 Sample response: For a magazine article on public attitudes about hunting, a group that seeks to ban hunting might sample only an urban population. Since many urban residents may have only limited experience with hunting, the sample would not accurately represent the views of the population as a whole.

* * * * *

2.6 **a.** Sample response: Starting with the 2nd voter on list, select every 14th voter.

b. Sample response: Randomly generate 100 integers in the interval [1, 1400] and select voters corresponding to these numbers.

c. Sample response: Since 53% of the population is female, randomly select 53 female voters and 47 male voters.

2.7 **a.** The proposed method will not provide a simple random sample, since only the potential buyers who request a test drive are sampled.

b. Sample response: One advantage of the proposed method is that the sample would be easy to collect. This may make it more cost-effective for the manufacturer. One disadvantage is that the sample is biased against potential buyers who do not ask for a test drive.

* * * * * * * * * *

Activity 3

In this activity, students explore sampling as a tool for describing a population. Using frequency histograms, they investigate the distribution of sample proportions.

Materials List

- two varieties of dry beans of different colors but similar sizes (approximately 150 beans per group)
- paper bags or other opaque containers (one per group)
- markers (optional; one per group)

Teacher Note

The two types of beans should be distinguishable by color but not by size—for example, kidney beans and pinto beans. As an alternative, students may place a clearly discernible mark on 40% of the beans. Objects other than beans also may be used as long, as they are of similar size and shape and can be divided into two distinct groups.

Technology

- statistics package
- spreadsheet (optional)
- programmable calculator (optional)

Teacher Note

In Part **f** of the exploration, students use technology to simulate sampling. If a statistics package that allows sampling using binomial trials is not available, students may use a spreadsheet or a programmable calculator.

For example, the following program was written for the TI-92 calculator. It stores the results of each sample as an element of a list in the variable *list1*. (Each student should input a different seed number before running the program.)

```
:Sampling( )
:Prgm
:  ClrIO:DelVar list1
:  Input "Known Percentage?", p
:  Input "Number of samples?", n
:  Input "Sample size?", s
:  0→c
:  For i,1,n
:      Disp "Sample number", i
:      For j,1,s
:          rand(100)→r
:          If r<p Then
:              c+1→c
:          EndIf
:      EndFor
:      int(100*(c/s)+0.5)→list1[i]
:      0→c
:      Disp "Percent marked:", list1[i]
:  EndFor
:EndPrgm
```

To use a spreadsheet to simulate sampling from a population in which 40% have a particular characteristic, complete the following steps.

- Enter "1" in the first 40 rows in column 1.
- Enter "0" in the next 60 rows in column 1.
- Enter random numbers in each of the first 100 rows of column 2.
- Sort the random numbers, allowing each value in column 1 to follow its corresponding random number.
- To select a sample of size *n*, find the sum of the values in the first *n* rows of column 1. This sum represents the number of individuals in the sample with the given characteristic.

The spreadsheet below shows how this method was used to simulate a sample of size 10 from such a population.

0	0.97677807	
0	0.94181197	
0	0.9394662	sum = 4
1	0.91934078	
1	0.91402806	
0	0.88979734	
0	0.87726297	
1	0.85729261	
1	0.82452538	
0	0.80195173	
⋮	⋮	

Exploration

This exploration is intended for small groups. In Part **e**, the class will combine their data to obtain a larger pool of samples.

a. Students do not need to create a population of 2380 beans. Approximately 150 beans is sufficient, as long as the population proportion is 40%.

b. Since 40% of 25 is 10, it would be reasonable to expect about 10 beans to be marked.

c–d. Sample data:

Sample	Percentage of Marked Beans
1	48
2	32
3	36
4	48
5	48
6	60
7	56
8	48
9	40
10	36

e.

1. Sorting the data should simplify the task of determining the number of sample proportions that fall within a given interval.
2. The mean of the sample proportions should be close to the population proportion of 40%.
3. Sample histogram for class data:

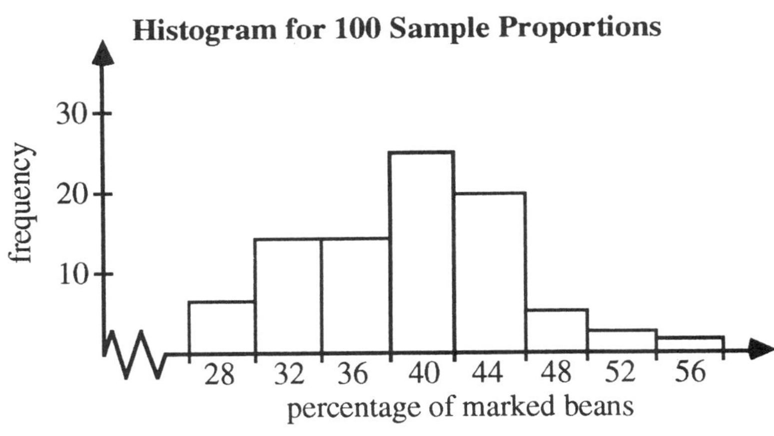

4. In the sample data shown above, 23% of the sample proportions are less than 32%.

f. The results of a simulation using technology should be reasonably close to the results obtained using a population of beans.

Discussion

a. Sample response: Both graphs have peaks near the mean of the sample proportions, then gradually taper off on each side.

b. The mean of the sample proportions should be close to 40%, the population proportion.

c.
1. Sample response: The histograms would be similar in shape, but would be centered about the population proportion of 52%.
2. If twice as many samples were taken, the histogram would still be centered about the mean and have the same basic shape.

e. To obtain a more accurate characterization of the population, students may suggest increasing the sample size.

d. Students should observe that the percentage of sample proportions less than or equal to 32% provides an estimate of the probability of obtaining such a sample from a population in which the population proportion is 40%.

1. Responses will vary. In one simulation of 90 samples of size 25, 23% were less than or equal to 32%. In another simulation, 26% were less than or equal to 32%.
2. Sample response: The simulation models a situation in which Amelia is preferred by 40% of student voters. The selected sample showed only 32% support for her candidacy. This is at the lower end of the simulated samples from a population with 40% support. Since this indicates that obtaining a sample with 32% support from a population with 40% support is not very likely, Amelia should be concerned.

Assignment

***3.1**

a. Of those surveyed, 36% (9 of 25) indicated that they would vote for the pool.

b. There are 300 samples in the simulation.

c. The mean percentage of "yes" votes may be estimated by dividing the sum of the products of each frequency and its corresponding percentage by the total number of samples. The mean of the sample proportions in the simulation is about 52%.

d. Sample response: The architect should not be hired. The simulation models a population that would just barely pass the proposal. The town's single sample of 25 voters revealed only 36% support, which is at the extreme low end of the simulated samples from a population with 51% support. The town's sample is very unlikely to have come from a population with enough votes to pass the proposal.

3.2 **a.** Sample response: Since 10% of the population will not vote, Amelia must obtain a majority of the remaining 90%. Therefore, she would need approximately 46% to win.

b. The following sample histogram shows the results of 90 samples of size 25 taken from a population with an assumed parameter of 46%.

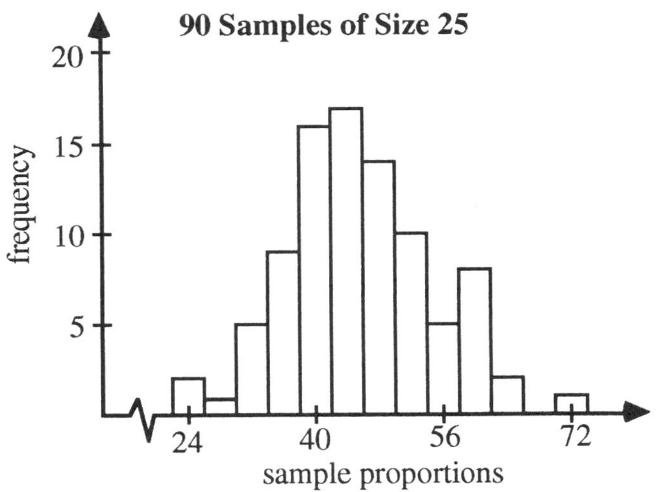

c. In the histogram in Part **c**, 8 of the 90 samples, or approximately 9%, have a sample proportion of less than 32%.

d. Sample response: If Amelia actually has 46% support, the probability of selecting a sample of 25 students with 8 or fewer in favor of Amelia is fairly small. Amelia's chances of winning the election are not encouraging. Since there were a large number of undecided voters in the census, however, Amelia still has a chance of winning.

* * * * *

3.3 a–b. The following histogram shows the results for 300 samples of size 5 for a simulation of a fair die.

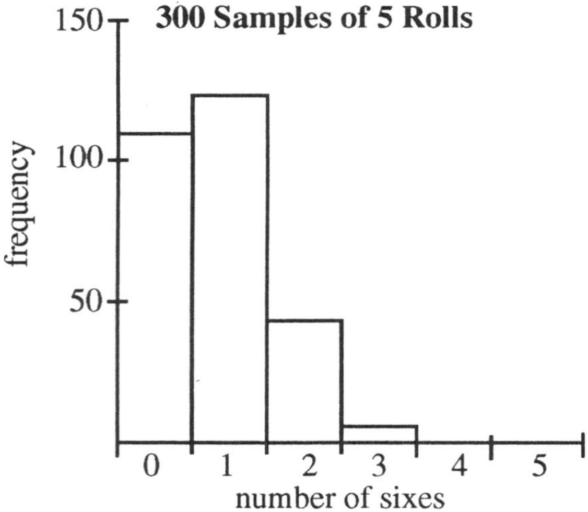

c. Answers will vary. In the sample data shown in Parts **a** and **b**, the estimated probability is 0. **Note:** The theoretical probability of rolling a six 4 out of 5 times with a fair die is approximately 0.6%.

d. Sample response: No. The die does not appear to be fair. Although rolling a six 4 out of 5 times is possible, it is very unlikely.

* * * * * * * * * *

Activity 4

In this activity, students determine the maximum standard deviation of all possible sample proportions for samples of any size. They then use this value to describe the interval for a confidence statement.

Materials List

- none

Technology

- graphing utility
- spreadsheet
- statistics package
- programmable calculator (optional)

Teacher Note

To save time in Exploration **1**, you may wish to ask some students to complete Parts **a** and **b**, some to complete Part **c**, and some to complete Part **d**.

Exploration 1

a. **1.** Using a statistics package that allows binomial simulations, students should generate 90 samples of size 25, with a probability of success of 0.40. (See teacher note in Activity **3** if this technology is not available.)

2. Sorting the data should simplify the task of determining the percentage of sample proportions that fall within 1 or 2 standard deviations of the population proportion.

3. Sample histogram:

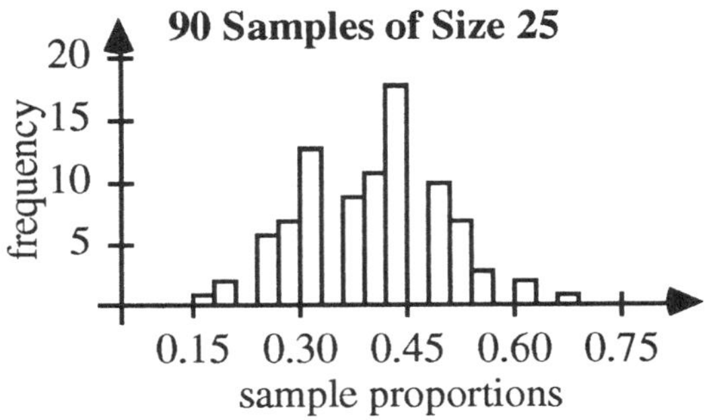

b. **1.** Using the formula given in the mathematics note, the standard deviation of all possible sample proportions is:

$$\sqrt{\frac{0.4(1-0.4)}{25}} \approx 0.098$$

or about 9.8%.

2. In the sample data shown in Part **a**, 69% of the sample proportions were contained in the interval [30.2, 49.8].

3. In the sample data shown in Part **a**, 98% of the sample proportions were contained in the interval [20.4, 59.6].

c. The following histogram shows the results of 90 samples of size 50.

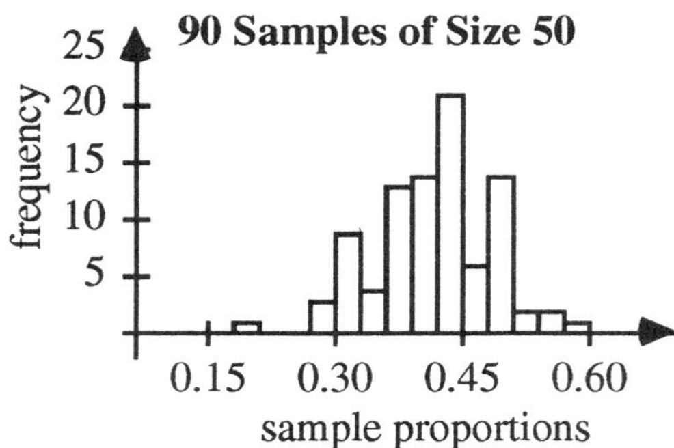

Using the formula given in the mathematics note, the standard deviation of all possible sample proportions is:

$$\sqrt{\frac{0.4(1-0.4)}{50}} \approx 0.069 = 6.9\%$$

For the sample data shown above, 69% of the sample proportions were contained in the interval [33.1,46.9], and 98% were contained in the interval [26.2,53.8].

d. The following histogram shows the results of 90 samples of size 100.

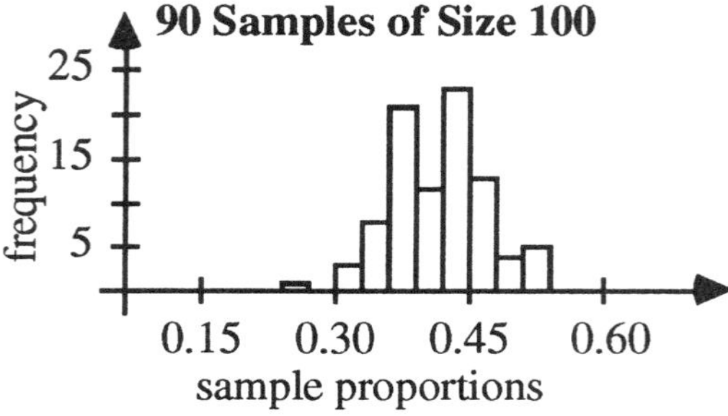

Using the formula given in the mathematics note, the standard deviation of all possible sample proportions is:

$$\sqrt{\frac{0.4(1-0.4)}{100}} \approx 0.049 = 4.9\%$$

For the sample data shown above, 68% of the sample proportions were contained in the interval [35.1, 44.9], and 94% were contained in the interval [30.2,49.8].

Discussion 1

a. The histograms should display approximately the same mean of the sample proportions (40%), although their shapes may vary.

b.
1. As the sample size increases, the sample proportions tend to be closer to the mean.
2. As the sample size increases, the standard deviation of all possible sample proportions decreases.
3. As the sample size increases, the interval that represents values within 1 standard deviation of the population proportion becomes narrower.

c.
1. For a sample size of 25, the percentages may vary. They should be relatively close—approximately 68% and 95%—for the larger sample sizes.
2. Sample response: They indicate an estimated probability that the sample proportion will be within 1 or 2 standard deviations of the population proportion.

d. Answers will vary. For a sample size of 100, a sample proportion of 32% is more than 1 standard deviation from the population proportion. In the sample data given in Exploration **1**, only 5% of the samples yielded a proportion of 32% or less. This suggests that Amelia should be very concerned about her support, since the sample is not likely to have come from a population in which 40% favored her.

Exploration 2

In this exploration, students use the formula for the standard deviation of all possible sample proportions to examine the maximum standard deviation for a given sample size. This value is a conservative estimate of the standard deviation of all possible sample proportions for a situation in which the actual population proportion is unknown.

a.
1. Sample graph:

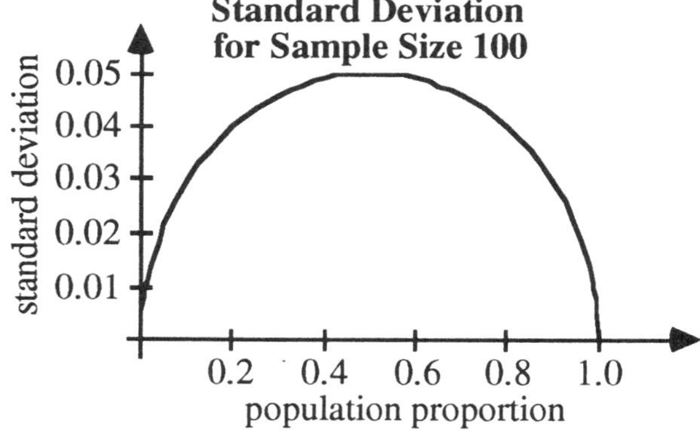

2. Students may use the trace function on a graphing utility to find that the maximum standard deviation is 0.05.

3. The population proportion that corresponds with the maximum standard deviation is 0.5.

b. After repeating Part **a** for other sample sizes, students should conjecture that the maximum standard deviation always occurs when the population proportion is 0.5. As the sample size increases, the maximum standard deviation decreases.

c–d. Students add and subtract 5% from each sample proportion to obtain 90 intervals, then determine how many of these intervals contain the known population proportion of 40%.

e. The percentage of intervals that contain the population proportion should be close to 68%.

f. For a sample size of 100, 2 • MSD = 10%. The percentage of intervals that contain the population proportion should be near 95%.

Discussion 2

a. The domain of the function is $0 \le p \le 1$, the range is $0 \le \sigma \le 0.05$.

b. Sample response: I would be more confident predicting that the population proportion is within 2 MSDs of the sample proportion. According to the results of the simulation, about 95% of those intervals contained the known population proportion.

c. Sample response: It is important to use the maximum standard deviation because this value describes the largest possible interval, thereby reducing the chance of error.

d. Sample response: Since the width of the intervals depends on the MSD, and the MSD is calculated using the formula $0.5/\sqrt{n}$, increasing the sample size would make the intervals narrower, while decreasing the sample size would make the intervals wider.

e. Sample response: I would be more confident in predicting the population proportion using the larger sample size. For a sample size of 100, the MSD is 5%. This means the sample proportion would be within 10% of the true proportion about 95% of the time.

For a sample size of 400, the MSD is $0.5/\sqrt{400}$ or 2.5%. The value of 2 MSDs is $2(2.5\%)$ or 5%. This means that the sample proportion would be within 5% of the true proportion about 95% of the time.

f. 1. When the margin of error is twice the maximum standard deviation, it decreases as the sample size increases.

2. Since the maximum standard deviation of all possible sample proportions is not affected by the size of the population, neither is the margin of error.

g. Using a value of twice the maximum standard deviation, the margin of error for a sample size of 1500 is approximately 2.6%. Therefore, the pollster can be confident that the statistic is within 2.6% of the parameter.

Assignment

4.1 **a.** For a sample size of 400, the maximum standard deviation of all possible sample proportions is 2.5%. Therefore, it is highly likely that the proportion of the population that will vote for Amelia is between 44% and 54%.

b. Sample response: Since 10% of the student body does not intend to vote, Amelia only needs the support of 46% of the population in order to win. Since it is very likely (about 95% probability) that the population proportion falls within the 44% to 54% interval, her prospects are very good but not guaranteed.

4.2 Sample response: A confidence statement should not be made about this survey. The ratio of 4 to 5 does not give any indication of sample size.

4.3 Sample response: Although Senator Rodriguez is not assured of reelection, a victory is likely since the poll predicts a majority of at least 51% (54 – 3) with a high level of confidence.

***4.4** The margin of error for a sample of size 1500 is $1/\sqrt{1500} \approx 0.026$, which is less than 3%.

***4.5** Sample response: The margin of error for a sample of 100 is about 10%. Since Amelia only needs votes from 46% of the population to win, her election is highly likely.

* * * * *

4.6 The value of twice the maximum standard deviation of all possible sample proportions for $n = 40$ is:

$$2 \bullet \sigma = 2 \bullet \sqrt{\frac{0.5 \bullet (1 - 0.5)}{40}} = \frac{1}{\sqrt{40}} \approx 0.16$$

Using this value to determine the margin of error, the population proportion is likely to fall in the interval [0.67, 0.99].

4.7 The value of twice the maximum standard deviation of all possible sample proportions for $n = 25$ is:

$$1/\sqrt{25} = 0.2$$

This value corresponds with a margin of error of 20%.

* * * * * * * * * *

Answers to Summary Assessment

1. Answers will vary. Sample response: To sample the bulbs, I would use a systematic sampling method. Assuming about 10,000 bulbs are produced per day, I would select every 250th bulb. This would create an approximate sample size of 40, which would be practical and efficient in terms of time and money.

2. The following histogram shows the results of 100 samples of size 40 from a population in which $p = 0.05$:

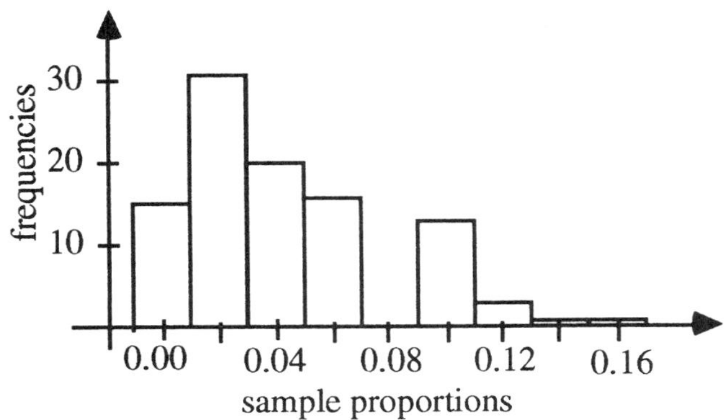

3. Using the value of twice the maximum standard deviation of all possible sample proportions, the margin of error for a sample size of 40 is:

$$\frac{1}{\sqrt{40}} \approx 0.158$$

4. Judging from the results of the simulation, the experimental probability of obtaining a sample with at least 6% defective bulbs from a population in which $p = 0.05$ is about 35%.

   Given a sample proportion of 6.2%, the population proportion is highly likely to be contained in the interval [0, 22.0%]. Since this interval is very wide, I would take another sample of the day's production using a larger sample size. If this sample also resulted in a proportion of defective bulbs greater than 5%, I would check to make sure that the equipment is running properly.

Module Assessment

1. The administration at Washington High is reviewing the student dress code. Before recommending any changes, the principal has agreed to allow the student council to conduct a survey of student opinion. Three members of the council have suggested sampling methods for the poll.

   Proposal A involves selecting the first student that walks into the gym at the next school-wide assembly and every 15th student after that.

   Proposal B uses a computer program to generate random numbers with the same number of digits as student identification numbers. Those students whose identification numbers match the computer-generated numbers will be selected for the poll.

   Proposal C recommends selecting 10 freshmen, 10 sophomores, 10 juniors, and 10 seniors for the poll.

   a. Identify the strengths and weaknesses of each proposal.

   b. Which proposal seems most fair? Justify your choice.

   c. Describe any bias that might exist in the proposal you chose in Part **b**.

2. **a.** Consider an experiment that involves flipping a fair coin 50 times. Use a simulation to estimate the probability that less than 40% of the flips will be heads.

   b. Imagine that you flipped a dime 400 times and recorded 170 heads. Would you conclude that this dime is not a fair coin? Explain your response.

3. Which statistic would you have more confidence in: a proportion from a simple random sample of 200 people or one from a sample of 500 people? Justify your response using the standard deviation of all possible sample proportions.

4. An independent polling company asked a random sample of 588 teenagers the following question: "What brand of court shoes do you prefer?" Of those surveyed, 174 responded "Eagle Wing." Write a confidence statement describing the results of the poll.

Answers to Module Assessment

1. **a.** Proposal A is an example of systematic sampling. This method provides an easy way to gather data. However, since all students who do not attend the assembly are automatically excluded, it creates a biased sample. If all students do attend, then it gives a relatively large sample—158 students. Using a value of twice the maximum standard deviation of all possible sample proportions, the margin of error for that sample size is about 8%.

   Proposal B is an example of random sampling. Although it may involve some time and effort to create the computer program, it should generate an unbiased sample. However, there is no way to know how many students will be selected for the sample, and no way to estimate the margin of error.

   Proposal C is an example of stratified sampling. Although it gives each class equal representation in the sample, it may not generate a sample that is representative of the school population. For example, if the freshman class is substantially larger than the senior class, the sample is biased against freshmen. It also provides a relatively small sample—only 40 students. The margin of error for that sample size is about 16%.

   b–c. Answers will vary. Since it has the least potential for bias, some students may select proposal B and specify a sample size. For a large sample, the margin of error will be relatively small.

2. **a.** Answers will vary. In one simulation, the proportion of heads was less than 40% in 7 of 90 samples. This corresponds with an estimated probability of 8%.

   b. Sample response: The sample proportion is 170/400 or 42.5%. Using $1/\sqrt{n}$ to determine a margin of error, it is highly likely that the true proportion is between 37.5% and 47.5%. Therefore, I would guess that either this dime is not a fair coin, or the flipping process is somehow biased.

3. Students should be more confident in the results obtained using a sample size of 500. The value of twice the maximum standard deviation of all possible sample proportions for this sample size is approximately 4.5%. This means that the population proportion is very likely to be within 4.5% of the sample proportion. The corresponding margin of error for a sample size of 200 is about 7.1%.

4. The sample proportion is 174/588 or about 30%. Using $1/\sqrt{n}$ to determine a margin of error, it is highly likely that between 26% and 34% of all teenagers prefer Eagle Wing brand court shoes.

Selected References

Gallup, G. *The Sophisticated Poll Watcher's Guide*. Ephrata, PA: Princeton Opinion Press, 1972.

Landwehr, J. M., J. Swift, and A. E. Watkins. *Exploring Surveys and Information from Samples*. Palo Alto, CA: Dale Seymour Publications, 1988.

Mizrahi, A., and M. Sullivan. *Finite Mathematics with Applications for Business and Social Sciences*. New York: John Wiley & Sons, 1973.

Moore, D. S. *Statistics: Concepts and Controversies*. New York: W. H. Freeman and Co., 1991.

Sincich, T. *Statistics by Example*. San Francisco, CA: Dellen Publishing Company, 1982.

Flashbacks

Activity 1

1.1 Find the mean and standard deviation of the following set of numbers:

$$\{345, 642, 521, 745, 548, 367\}$$

1.2 A box contains 100 kidney beans, 64 black beans, and 96 lima beans.

a. What percentage of the beans in the box are black beans?

b. What percentage are kidney beans?

Activity 2

2.1 Describe a method of randomly generating 20 integers from 1 to 10.

Activity 3

3.1 What number is 40% of 360?

3.2 Write each of the following percentages as a decimal.

a. 34%

b. 0.4%

3.3 Write each of the following decimals as a percentage.

a. 0.52

b. 0.0334

3.4 The following histogram shows the number of hot dogs sold by a vendor each day for seven days.

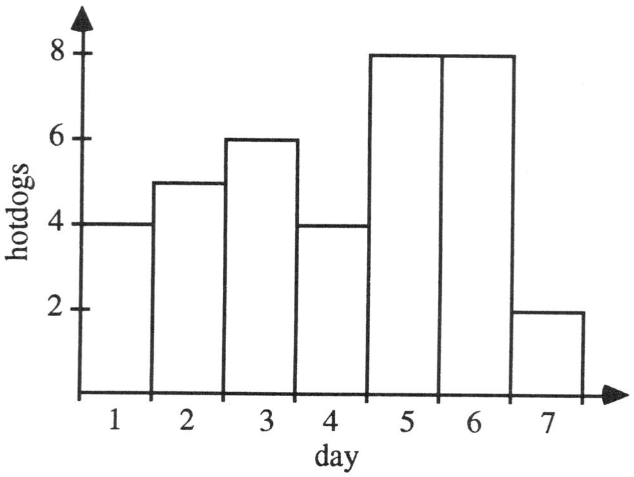

a. Find the mean number of hot dogs sold per day.

b. Calculate the percentage of hot dogs sold on or before day 3.

Activity 4

4.1 Terry caught 18 fish on her first day of fishing, 16 on her second day, 22 on her third day, 10 on her fourth day, and 14 on her last day. Create a bar graph that shows the number of fish she caught each day.

4.2 List the integers that are included in the interval [3.1, 7.2].

Answers to Flashbacks

Activity 1

1.1 The mean of the numbers is 528; the standard deviation is approximately 141.

1.2 **a.** approximately 25%

b. approximately 38%

Activity 2

2.1 To randomly generate integers from 1 to 10, students may suggest drawing numbered slips of paper from a bowl, rolling a 10-sided die, or using technology. On a TI-92 calculator, for example, the command "rand(10)" generates a random integer between 1 and 10.

Activity 3

3.1 144

3.2 **a.** 0.34

b. 0.004

3.3 **a.** 52%

b. 3.34%

3.4 **a.** approximately 5.3 hot dogs

b. approximately 41%

Activity 4

4.1 Sample graph:

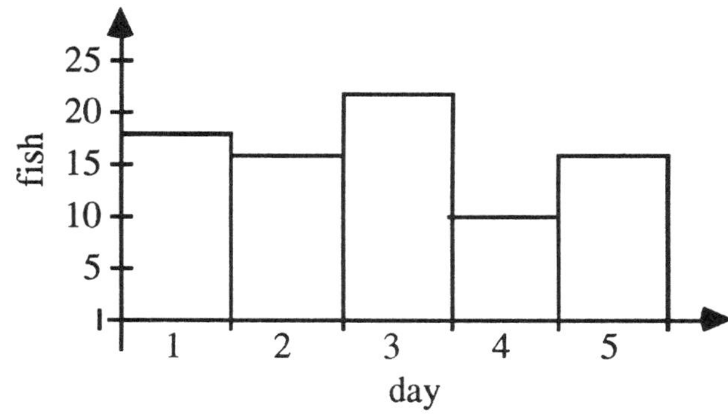

4.2 3, 4, 5, 6, 7

Town Map

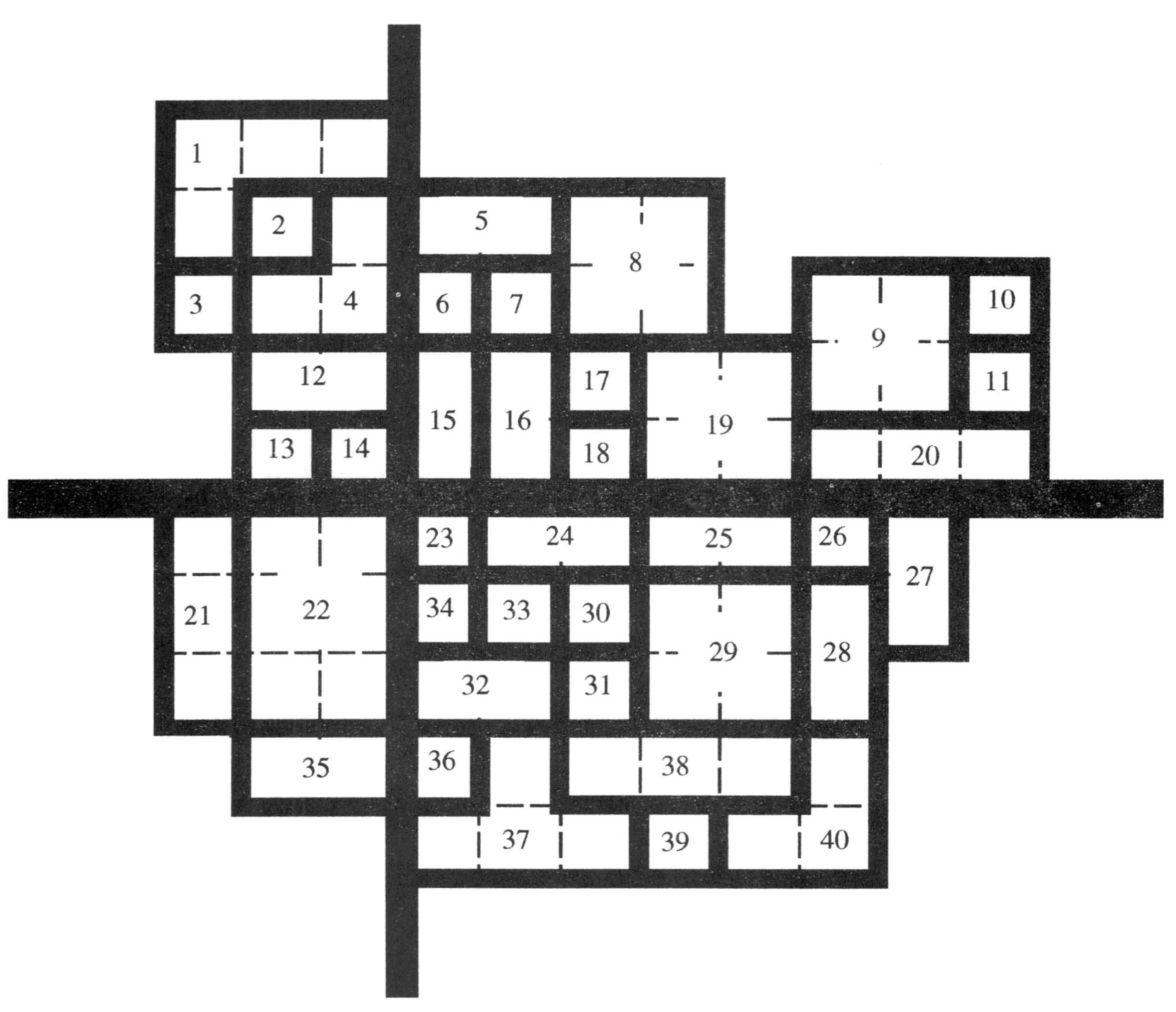
1
2
5
8
3
4
6
7
9
10
12
17
11
15
16
19
13
14
18
20
23
24
25
26
27
21
22
34
33
30
29
28
32
31
35
36
38
37
39
40

Traditional Design

In this module, you examine the geometric properties of some traditional American Indian art forms.

Todd Fife • Anne Merrifield

Teacher Edition
Traditional Design

Overview

This module uses traditional American Indian art to examine basic geometric principles. Students use the lone-star quilts of the Assiniboine and Sioux tribes to explore parallel and perpendicular lines. They then use the medicine wheels of the Northern Cheyenne to explore properties of tangents and secants in relation to a circle. Finally, they use Navajo sandpaintings to explore transformations.

Objectives

In this module, students will:

- use paper-folding constructions to examine angle bisectors, perpendicular lines, parallel lines, and midpoints
- explore properties of angles formed by parallel lines and a transversal
- explore geometric rep tiles
- identify relationships between tangents and secants
- examine properties of parallelograms (specifically rhombi)
- examine similar triangles created by dilations.

Prerequisites

For this module, students should know:

- the definition of supplementary angles
- line and rotational symmetry
- properties of a square
- properties of reflections, dilations, rotations, and translations.

Time Line

Activity	Intro.	1	2	3	Summary Assessment	Total
Days	1	2	2	2	1	8

Materials Required

Materials	Activity				
	Intro.	1	2	3	Summary Assessment
straightedge	X	X	X	X	X
scissors		X			
protractor	X			X	
template A	X				
template B		X			
template C		X			
template D			X		
template E			X		
template F			X		
template G				X	
template H				X	
template I					X

Teacher Note

Blackline masters of the templates appear at the end of this teacher edition.

Technology

Software	Activity				
	Intro.	1	2	3	Summary Assessment
geometry utility		X	X	X	

Traditional Design

Introduction

Students develop paper-folding methods to construct angle bisectors, perpendicular lines, parallel lines, and midpoints.

Materials List

- template A (one copy per student)
- straightedge (one per student)
- protractor (one per student)

Exploration

Each student will require a copy of template A to complete the exploration.

a. **1.** Student papers should resemble the following diagram:

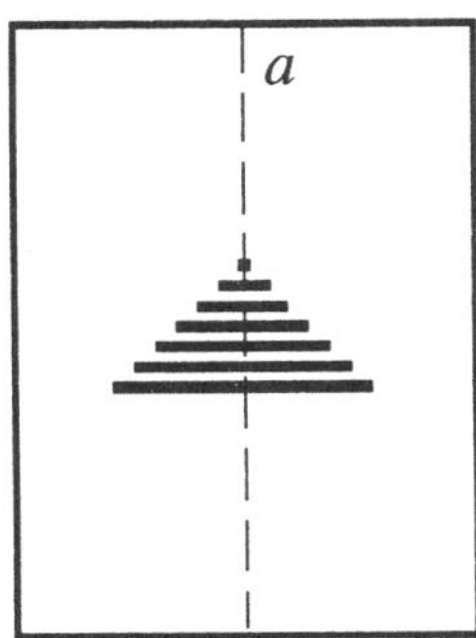

2. Each bar is divided in half by the crease.

3. Sample response: The line of symmetry is the perpendicular bisector of each bar in the symbol.

b. **1.** Students should fold the paper so that the line of symmetry coincides with itself, creating a crease parallel to the bars. Student papers should resemble the following diagram:

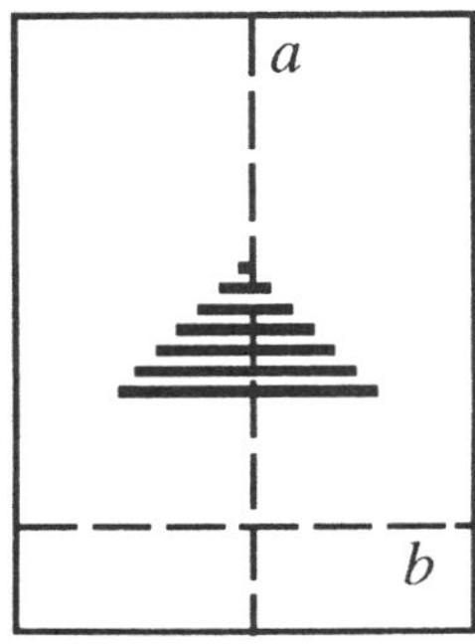

2. Student papers should resemble the following diagram:

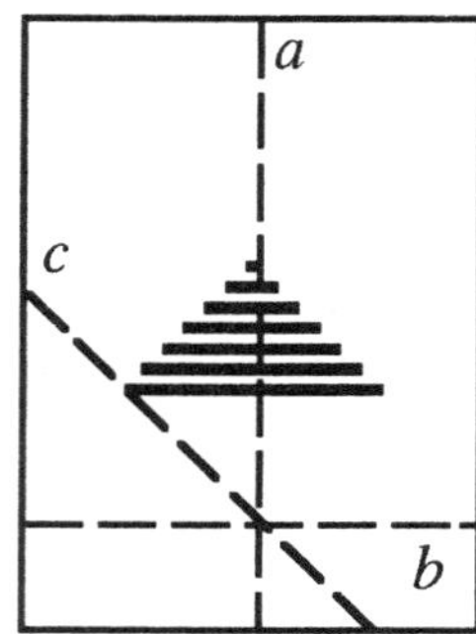

c. 1. The two perpendicular distances should be equal.

2. The measure of each angle is 45°.

3. Sample response: Crease c is the bisector of an angle formed by creases a and b.

Discussion

a. 1. Sample response: An object can be reflected by folding along a line of reflection, then tracing to show the reflected image.

2. The perpendicular bisector of a segment can be found by folding one of the segment's endpoints onto the other.

3. The angle bisector can be found by folding one side of an angle so that it coincides with the other side of the angle. (See Figure **3** in the student edition.)

4. The midpoint of a line segment can be found by creating a perpendicular bisector. The intersection of the perpendicular bisector and the segment is the midpoint.

b. As shown in the following diagram, a square can be formed from a rectangular sheet of paper by creating the angle bisector of one of the 90° corners. The part of the paper that is not doubled can then be cut off, leaving a square.

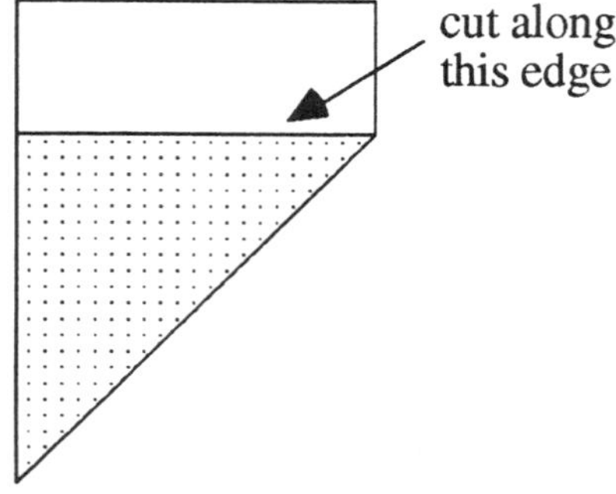

Activity 1

Students use the design of a star quilt to review the properties of angles formed from parallel lines cut by a transversal. They also examine the properties of a rhombus and explore how to create geometric rep tiles.

Materials List

- straightedge (one per student)
- pair of scissors (one per student)
- copy of template B (one per student)
- copy of template C (one per student)

Discussion 1

a. Other than the eight-pointed star, students should recognize some parallelograms—including rhombi—in the design. They may also mention other shapes, such as the octagon that can be made by connecting the star's eight outer vertices.

b. A parallelogram—specifically, a rhombus—is the basic shape used to construct the star.

c. A rhombus is a parallelogram with congruent sides. **Note:** You may want students to discuss the properties of parallelograms as well. In the following exploration, students should also discover these properties of a rhombus: opposite angles are congruent, the diagonals are perpendicular bisectors of each other, and the diagonals bisect the angles.

Exploration

Students use paper folding to form a rhombus and explore some of its properties. Although students also may complete this construction using a geometry utility, this activity is designed to reflect the historical methods used by quiltmakers.

a. A square can be formed from a rectangular sheet of paper by creating the angle bisector of one of the 90° corners. The part of the paper that is not doubled is then cut off. (See Part **b** of the discussion in the introduction.)

b. Student papers should resemble the shape shown in Figure **6b** of the student edition.

c. As shown in Figure **7**, the resulting shape is a rhombus.

d. **1.** Students should not have to use protractors to measure these angles. The measure of each of the two smaller angles of the rhombus is the sum of two angles whose measures are:

$$\frac{1}{2}\left(\frac{1}{2}\bullet 90^{\circ}\right)=22.5^{\circ}$$

The sum is therefore 45°. The adjacent angles of the rhombus are supplementary to these 45° angles. Thus, each has a measure of 135°. **Note:** Students should recall supplementary angles from middle school. You may wish to remind them of the definition, or to draw and measure a few such angles on a geometry utility.

2. The opposite angles of a rhombus (and, in general, a parallelogram) are congruent.

e. The diagonals of the rhombus are perpendicular bisectors of each other. As seen from the construction of this rhombus, the diagonals also bisect the interior angles.

f. **1.** The midpoint of a line segment can be found by folding one of the segment's endpoints onto the other to create the segment's perpendicular bisector. The intersection of the perpendicular bisector and the segment is the midpoint.

2. Two congruent parallelograms are formed. Student papers should resemble the diagram below.

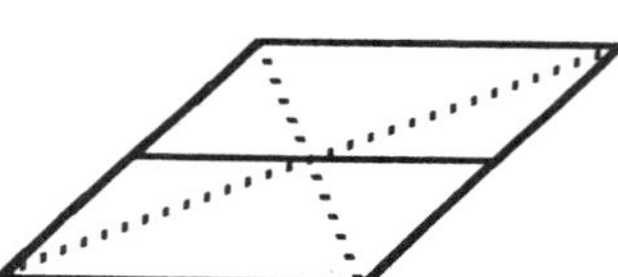

3. Student papers should resemble the following diagram.

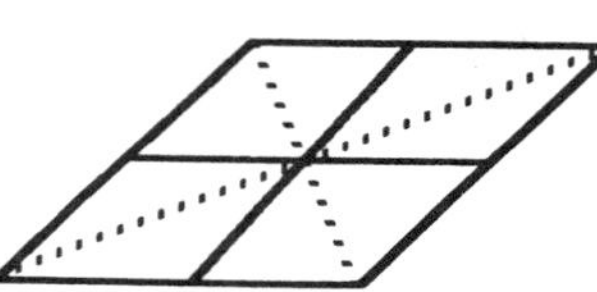

g. Four smaller rhombi are formed, each similar to the original rhombus.

h. The measures of the interior angles of the smaller rhombi are the same as those of the original rhombus: 45° and 135°.

Discussion 2

a. Sample response: Yes, the shapes are similar to the original rhombus. The corresponding sides are proportional and the corresponding angles are congruent. **Note:** You may want to ask students what information is necessary to determine if two rhombi are similar. If one angle of a rhombus is congruent to one angle of another rhombus, then the two rhombi are similar.

b. The two parallelograms are congruent. Since they are formed by joining the midpoints of opposite sides of a rhombus, the corresponding sides are congruent and the corresponding angles are congruent.

c. The diagonals of the rhombus are perpendicular bisectors of each other. As seen from the construction of the rhombus, the diagonals also bisect the interior angles.

d.

1. The opposite angles of a rhombus (and, in general, a parallelogram) are congruent. Adjacent angles are supplementary.
2. Sample response: One way to show congruence is to tear off the angles from the paper models and match them. Another way is to measure.

   One way to show supplementary angles is to tear off the angles and place them together at the vertices. The non-adjacent sides will form a straight line.

   Note: All of these methods are demonstrations. To prove that these relationships are true, students must work with congruent figures.

d.

1. The measures of angles 1 and 3 are equal.
2. The measures of angles 2 and 4 are equal. Angles 2 and 4 also have the same positional relationship as angles 1 and 3 because they are two non-adjacent angles formed by two intersecting lines.
3. Vertical angles are two non-straight, non-adjacent angles formed by two intersecting lines.
4. Students should identify many pairs of vertical angles. In the diagram below, these pairs include $\angle AOB$ and $\angle EOF$, $\angle BOD$ and $\angle FOH$, $\angle COD$ and $\angle GOH$, $\angle AOD$ and $\angle EOH$.

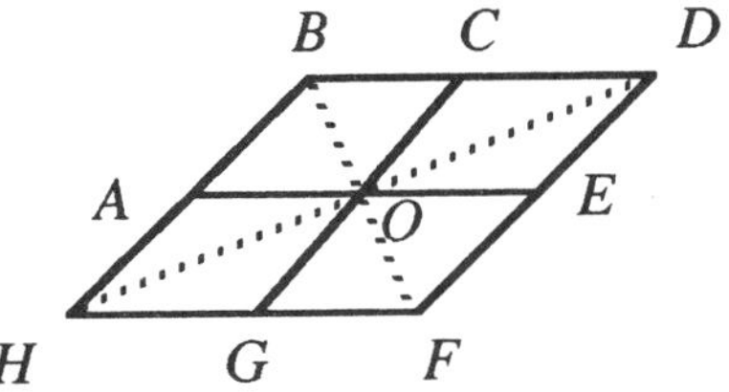

f. The result will resemble the diagram below. Each smaller rhombus is divided into four congruent rhombi. Each of these rhombi is similar to the original rhombus as well as the four intermediate rhombi from which they were formed.

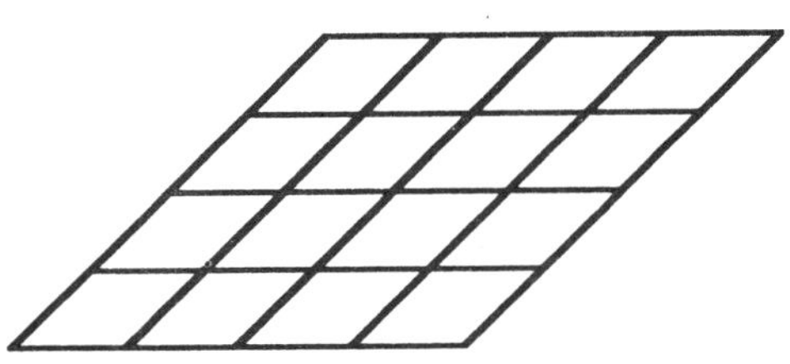

g. Sample response: Yes, because the original rhombus is divided into congruent rhombi, each similar to the original. **Note:** The self-similar nature of rep tiles is a feature common to many fractals. You may want to use this opportunity to introduce fractals through Sierpinski's triangle. (Students will examine Sierpinski's triangle in a research project in the Level 2 module, "Take It to the Limit.")

Teacher Note

To complete Problem **1.3**, each student will need a copy of template B. To complete Problem **1.4**, students will need a copy of template C. Blackline masters appear at the end of this teacher edition.

Assignment

1.1 a. Some students may want to simulate the paper folding on a geometry utility. Sample response:

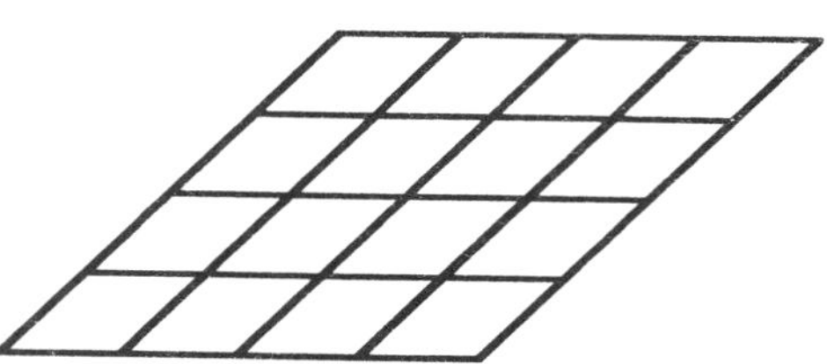

b. 1. Pairs of corresponding angles formed along a transversal of parallel lines are congruent.

2. There are four pairs of corresponding angles: $\angle 1$ and $\angle 5$, $\angle 2$ and $\angle 6$, $\angle 4$ and $\angle 8$, and $\angle 3$ and $\angle 7$.

3. Sample response: Corresponding angles are in the same relative position relative to parallel lines cut by a transversal. **Note:** Students should observe that a pair of corresponding angles can be above the parallel and on the same side of a transversal, or below the parallel and on the same side of the transversal. You may want to discuss the possibility of calling angles "corresponding" even if the lines are not parallel. In this case, however, the angles are not congruent.

c. There are four pairs of vertical angles: $\angle 1$ and $\angle 3$, $\angle 4$ and $\angle 2$, $\angle 5$ and $\angle 7$, and $\angle 6$ and $\angle 8$. The two angles in each pair are congruent.

d. 1. The measures of the two angles are equal.

2. The measures of the two angles are equal.

3. There are two pairs of alternate interior angles: $\angle 4$ and $\angle 6$, and $\angle 3$ and $\angle 5$. There are two pairs of alternate exterior angles: $\angle 1$ and $\angle 7$, and $\angle 2$ and $\angle 8$.

4. Sample response: Alternate interior angles are between the parallel lines and on opposite sides of a transversal. Alternate exterior angles are outside the parallel lines and on opposite sides of a transversal. With parallel lines, the respective pairs of angles are congruent. **Note:** You may want to discuss the fact that alternate interior angles formed when two nonparallel lines are cut by a transversal are not congruent. The alternate exterior angles in this situation are also not congruent.

1.2

a. Angle 1 and angle 3 are vertical angles. Angle 1 and angle 2 are supplementary angles. Angles 1 and 4 are also supplementary angles.

b. Sample response: Angles 1 and 5 are congruent because they are corresponding angles of two parallel lines cut by a transversal. Likewise, angles 1 and 13 are corresponding angles.

Angle 1 has the same measure as angle 9 because angle 9 and angle 5 are corresponding angles, or because angle 1 and angle 3 are vertical angles, while angle 3 and angle 9 are opposite angles of the rhombus.

c. Sample response: You only have to measure one angle to determine the measures of all of the angles at one vertex. Given the angles at one vertex, you can then determine the measures of all 16 angles in the diagram. therefore, the measures of all the angles can be found if you measure just one angle.

d. Sample response: It would be necessary to measure four angles, one angle at each vertex.

***1.3**

a. Students should observe that the two pieces are congruent. Some may want to cut the star along the line to compare pieces. **Note:** Students are not limited to existing lines in the design. They may draw any line that passes through the center of the star.

b. The two pieces have 180° rotational symmetry about the center of the star. They may also have symmetry about the line.

c. The two pieces will have 180° rotational symmetry about the center of the star for any line that passes through the center. If the line does not pass through the center and one of the outer vertices of the star, the pieces will not have symmetry with respect to the line.

d. Sample response: A line that passes through the center of the lone star design divides the star into two pieces that are the same size and the same shape. The two pieces are identical in design and are related by 180° rotational symmetry about the center of the star. Only those lines that pass through the center and one of the outer vertices of the star are lines of symmetry.

***1.4** **a.** Students may use lined notebook paper to help them draw sets of parallel lines. If the lines are perpendicular to the quilt strips, then the figures created are rectangles.

b. If the parallel lines are not perpendicular to the quilt strips, then the figures created are parallelograms.

c. $360°/8 = 45°$

d. Sample response: The quilter should draw a set of parallel lines that form 45° angles with the strips. These lines should be evenly spaced to form rhombi, as shown below.

Cutting along these parallel lines would create strips of rhombi. These new strips of material could then be shifted up or down one color and sewn to create the desired pattern. The eight large rhombi could then be cut from this new pattern. **Note:** Students should simulate this process using the paper template, scissors, and tape.

e. Sample response: The stitching may have been neither straight nor parallel. If the lines of stitches are not parallel, there is no guarantee that the corresponding angles will be congruent. As a result, the quilt may start to buckle or curl. To correct this, the seams would have to be taken out and re-sewn.

1.5 Student responses should resemble the following diagram:

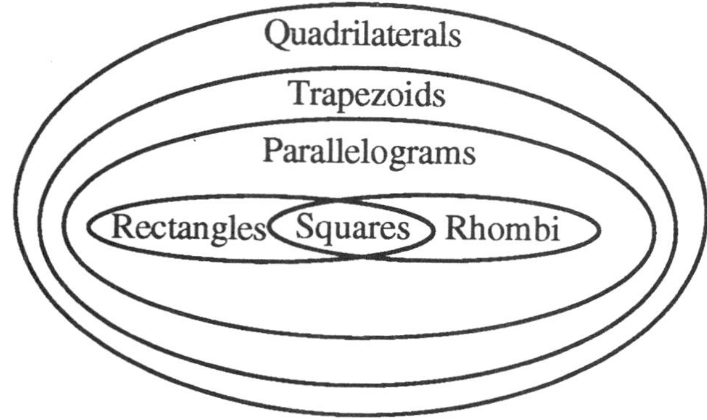

1.6 **a.** The diagonals do not bisect each other and are not perpendicular. They are not equal in length unless the trapezoid is isosceles.

b. The diagonals are not perpendicular but they do bisect each other. They are not equal in length.

c. The diagonals are equal in length. They are not perpendicular but they do bisect each other.

d. The diagonals are the perpendicular bisectors of each other. They also bisect the interior angles. The diagonals are not equal in length.

e. The diagonals are equal in length. They are the perpendicular bisectors of each other and also bisect the interior angles.

1.7 **a.** Sample drawing:

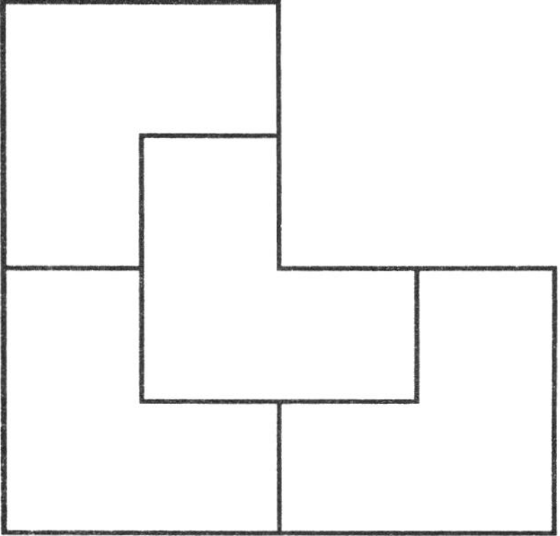

b. Sample response: I started with a triangle, found the midpoints of the sides, and connected them. This formed segments parallel to the corresponding sides of the original triangle and, in turn, four smaller triangles similar to the original. They are similar using the measures of corresponding and alternate interior angles as well as the sum of the measures of the angles of a triangle.

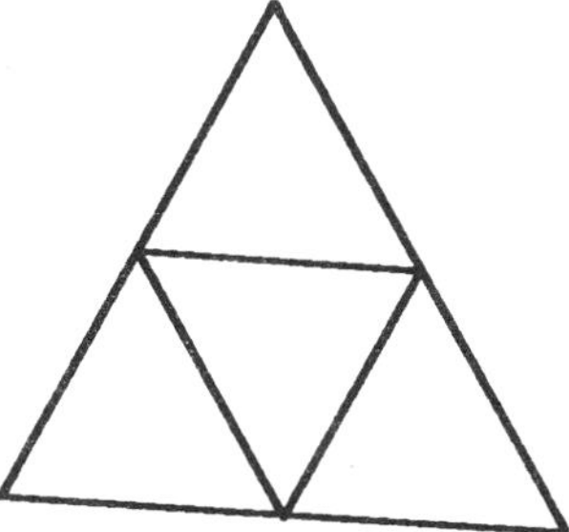

I then rotated the original triangle 180° about the midpoint of a side so that the original and the image formed a parallelogram. To make the quilt pattern, I used groups of parallelograms in the same way that the rhombus is used in the lone star quilt in Figure **5**.

* * * * *

1.8 Student responses may include some of the following methods.

1. Show that both pairs of opposite sides are the same length.
2. Show that both pairs of opposite sides are parallel.
3. Show that the diagonals bisect each other.
4. Show that both pairs of opposite angles are congruent.
5. Show that one pair of opposite sides is parallel and congruent.

1.9 Sample response: Measure the sides to determine if opposite sides have the same length. If they do, the quadrilateral is a parallelogram. Measure the diagonals to see if they are the same length. If they do, the parallelogram is a rectangle. **Note:** Students may also use the Pythagorean theorem to verify that the floor is a rectangle.

1.10 **a.** parallelogram, rhombus, rectangle, square

b. rhombus, square

c. rhombus, square

* * * * * * * * * *

Activity 2

Students use medicine wheel designs to explore properties of tangents and secants. They also use the properties of a circle to create their own medicine wheels.

Materials List

- copy of template D (one per student)
- copy of template E (one per student)
- copy of template F (one per student)
- straightedge

Technology

- geometry utility

Discussion 1

a. The medicine wheel displays rotational and line symmetries.

b. Sample response: Half of the symbol in the center could be constructed and reflected to create the other half. The larger circle is a dilation of the smaller one with center at the center of the circle. The quadrilaterals between the two concentric circles are all rotational images of another about the center. Each feather along the bottom of the wheel might be considered a translated image of the feather on the far right.

Exploration

Students use a geometry utility to investigate properties of chords, secants, and tangents. (This exploration also can be completed with a compass and straightedge.)

a. For best results, the diameter of the circle should be at least two-thirds the width of the screen.

b. **1.** See sample drawing given in Step **3** below.

2. Predictions may vary.

3. Sample drawing:

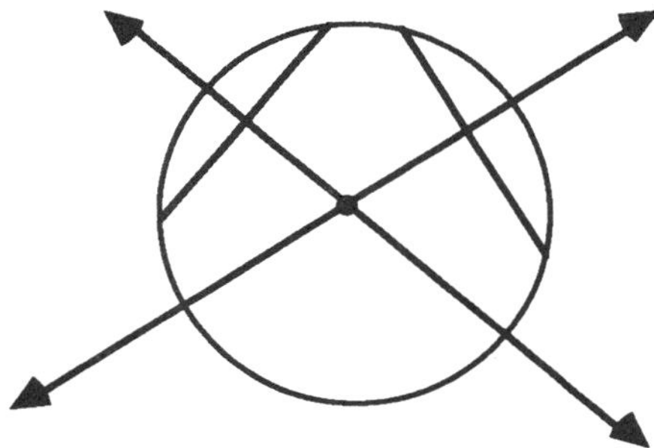

4–5. Students should observe that the perpendicular bisectors of chords intersect at the center of the circle.

c. Students should observe that when the angle has a measure of 90°, the line intersects the circle at a single point and is therefore a tangent line. The final sketch should resemble the following:

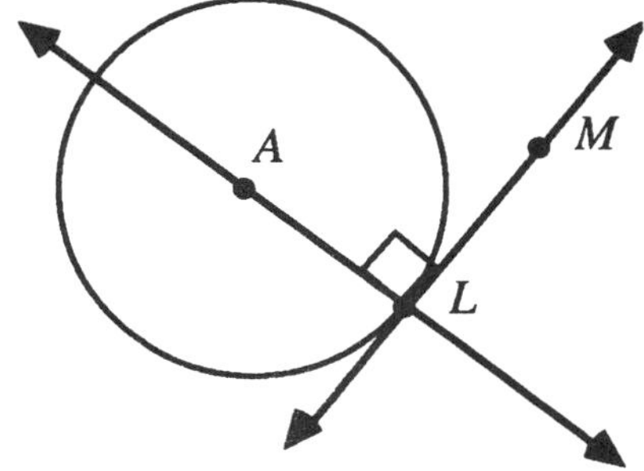

Teacher Note

Before discussing Part **d** below, you may wish to distribute copies of template D (one per student).

Discussion 2

a. **1.** 90°

2. The angle cannot measure 90°.

b. Sample response: A line tangent to a circle can be created by first folding a circle onto itself through a line containing the center of the circle. This fold represents a secant containing a diameter. Next, without unfolding the first fold, fold the crease onto itself where the first fold intersects the circle. This second fold creates a tangent line perpendicular to a diameter, through the point of tangency.

c. Sample response: The tangents are parallel. Two lines in the same plane perpendicular to the same line must be parallel to each other because alternate interior angles are congruent.

d. Sample response: The center of the circular plate can be found by drawing two chords and their perpendicular bisectors as shown in the sketch below. The intersection of the perpendicular bisectors is the center of the circle.

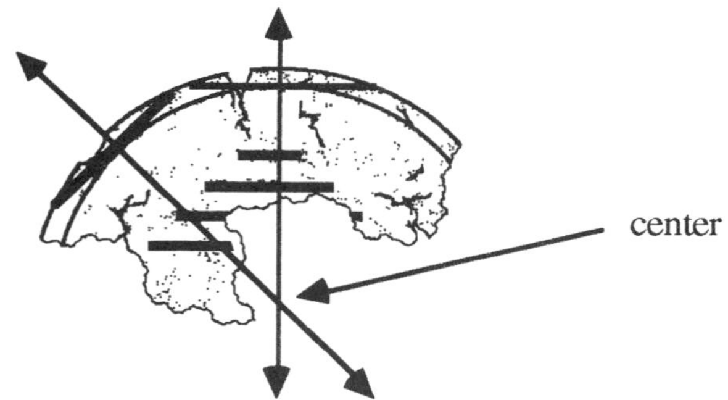

e. Sample response: Fold to create two chords on the circle. Fold to create the perpendicular bisector of each chord. The intersection of the perpendicular bisectors is the center of the circle.

f. The point of intersection of the perpendicular bisectors is the point equidistant from the four endpoints of the two chords. The center of a circle is the point that is equidistant from all points on the circle.

g. The altitude of an isosceles triangle is the perpendicular bisector of the base.

Teacher Note:

Each student will need a copy of template E to complete Problem **2.3** and a copy of template F to complete Problem **2.5**.

Assignment

2.1 a–b. Student methods will vary, depending on the technology used. Sample response: To draw each tangent, the radius containing both the point of the tangency and the center of the circle is constructed first. The tangent is then constructed as the line perpendicular to the radius and containing the point of tangency.

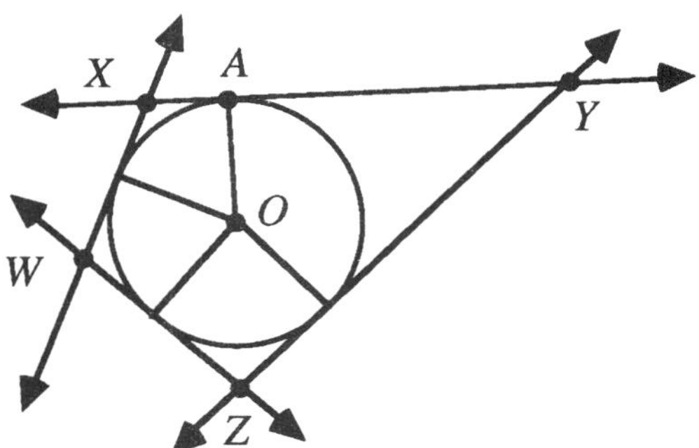

***2.2 a.** The following sample response refers to the labeled points in the diagram below: First, I constructed the circle with the larger radius. Then I constructed a point B on the circle. Point F was constructed by transforming B using a rotation of 60° around center A. Four more points were constructed using the same type of transformation for a total of six points. These form the vertices of a hexagon.

Next, I constructed the six sides of the hexagon (such as $\overline{BF}$) and the midpoints of each side (such as C). Then I drew the three segments connecting opposite pairs of midpoints (such as $\overline{CE}$). Finally, I constructed the circle with center A and radius $\overline{CA}$.

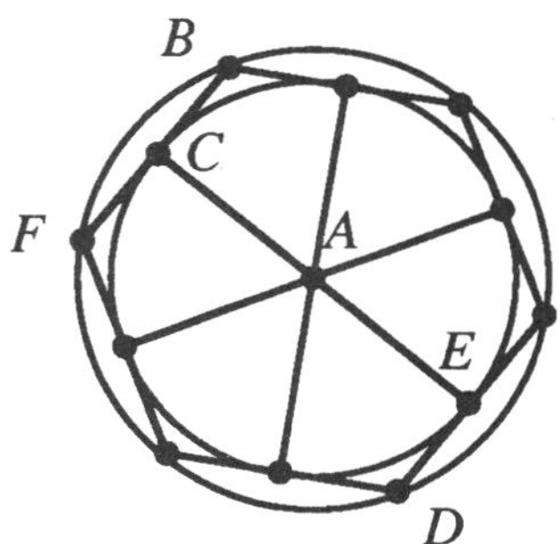

b. 1. The drawing has symmetry with respect to six lines: three that pass through the center of the circles and a pair of vertices of the hexagon (such as *B* and *D* in the sample diagram above); and three that pass through the center of the circles and a pair of midpoints of the sides of the hexagon (such as *C* and *E* in the diagram above).

2. The drawing has rotational symmetry around the center of the circles for any rotation of $n \bullet 60^\circ$, where n is an integer.

***2.3 a–b.** Students should find the center of the circle by constructing the perpendicular bisectors of at least two chords. Sample drawing:

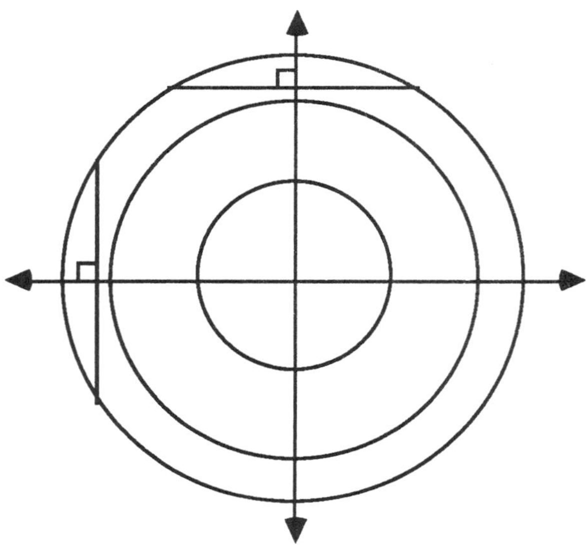

c. Selections will vary. Your school may already have a mascot or symbol.

d–e. Encourage students to be creative. They may want to display their wheels as a class.

2.4 **a.** Sample response: The center of the circle must be on the perpendicular bisector of $\overline{CC'}$ because all points contained on it are equidistant from C and C'.

b. Sample response: Draw the perpendicular bisector of $\overline{CC'}$ and the perpendicular bisector of $\overline{BB'}$. Their point of intersection is the center of rotation O.

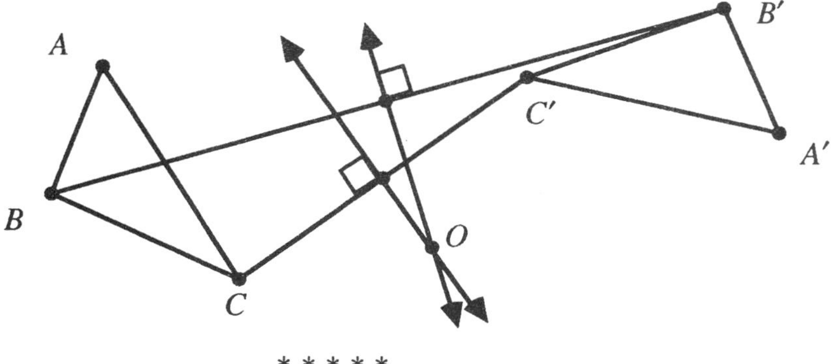

* * * * *

2.5 **a.** Since both chords include the center of the circle, they are diameters of the circle.

b. **1.** Sample response: Since $\overleftrightarrow{FI}$ and $\overleftrightarrow{GH}$ are tangent to the circle at B and E, respectively, the measures of $\angle JBA$ and $\angle LEA$ are both 90°. Since these two angles are congruent, they are alternate interior angles of the two parallel lines $\overleftrightarrow{FI}$ and $\overleftrightarrow{GH}$.

2. Using a similar argument to the one given above, students can show that $\overleftrightarrow{FG}$ and $\overleftrightarrow{IH}$ are parallel.

c. Although angle measures may vary among constructions, students should observe that $\angle KGP \cong \angle CGE$ and $\angle KGC \cong \angle CFB$. Sample response: $\angle KGP$ and $\angle CGE$ are vertical angles; $\angle KGC$ and $\angle CFB$ are alternate interior angles; and $\angle KGP$ and $\angle KGC$ are supplements.

d. Sample response:

Vertical Angles	Alternate Interior and Exterior Angles	Corresponding Angles
$\angle BID \cong \angle NIM$	$\angle BID \cong \angle IHL$	$\angle NIM \cong \angle DHL$
$\angle MID \cong \angle BIN$	$\angle MID \cong \angle DHE$	$\angle NIB \cong \angle DHE$
$\angle EHQ \cong \angle DHL$	$\angle NIB \cong \angle LHQ$	$\angle MID \cong \angle LHQ$
$\angle EHD \cong \angle QHL$	$\angle NIM \cong \angle EHQ$	$\angle BID \cong \angle EHQ$

e. Sample response: All four segments are congruent. Allowing for rounding errors, measurement supports this conjecture.

f. Sample response: Yes, *GFIH* is a rhombus because the lengths of $\overline{FI}$, $\overline{IH}$, $\overline{HG}$, and $\overline{GF}$ are the same, $\overline{FI}$ is parallel to $\overline{HG}$, and $\overline{IH}$ is parallel to $\overline{GF}$.

2.6 **a.** They are congruent isosceles triangles.

b. **1.** The two smaller angles are congruent. For example, consider the two angles formed by $\overline{CB}$. Since $\overline{CB}$ is a radius, it is perpendicular to the tangent at *B*. The incoming angle and outgoing angle are congruent. The sum of the incoming angle and $\angle ABC$ is 90°, as is the sum of the measures of the outgoing angle and $\angle DBC$. Therefore, $\angle ABC \cong \angle DBC$. A similar argument can be made at each of the other vertices.

2. angle bisector

c. Sample response: The outgoing angle at point *B* and $\angle BDA$ are alternate interior angles, where $\overleftrightarrow{BD}$ is a transversal. Since both angles measure 60°, the incoming ray and the tangent at point *D* must be parallel.

* * * * * * * * * *

Activity 3

Students use Navajo sandpaintings—along with similar triangles—to explore dilations.

Materials List

- template G (one copy per student)
- template H (one copy per student)

Technology

- geometry utility

Discussion 1

a. Sample response: Ignoring the feathers on the head, the design appears to have a vertical axis of symmetry. Some individual parts of the sandpainting also display line symmetry.

b. This design was constructed using two basic figures: rectangles and trapezoids.

c. Many of the geometric shapes which make up the sandpainting are similar to each other. For example, the trapezoids that make up the headdress are similar to each other and to the trapezoids that make up the hands, the arms, and the feet. These trapezoids are also similar to ones that form the garment worn around the waist of the figure, the design on the garment, and the tassels on the edge of the garment. The parallelograms that form the feathers in the headdress are similar to those that are found in the legs.

Exploration

In this exploration, students use similar triangles to explore the properties of dilations.

a. Sample drawing:

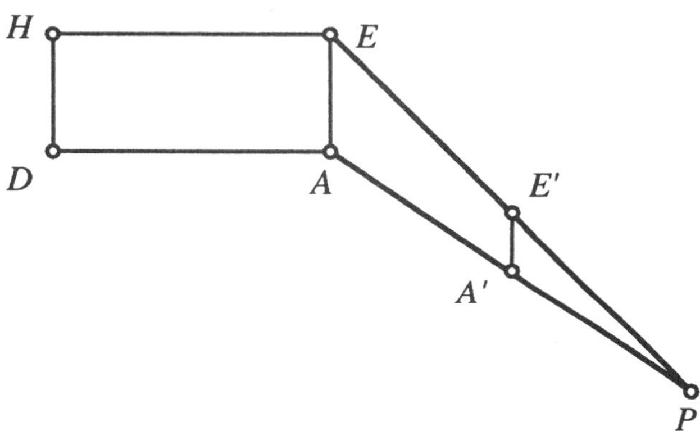

b. Because corresponding sides are proportional and corresponding angles are congruent, $\Delta PEA \sim \Delta PE'A'$.

c. Students complete a sketch of the image of *HEAD* under a dilation with center at *P*.

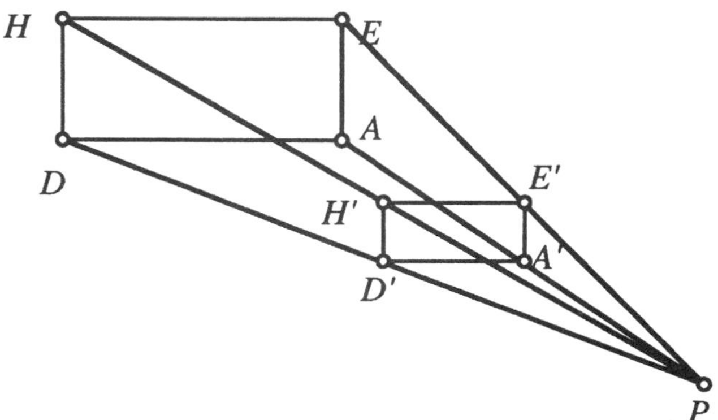

d. Dilations of polygons yield similar polygons. Angle measures and parallelism are preserved.

e. Sample response: Only the location of the image changes; its size stays the same.

f. Sample response: The lengths of the sides of the preimage, *HEAD*, would be reduced by a scale factor of 1/4 in the image, instead of 1/2.

Discussion 2

a.
1. The scale factor is 0.5.
2. The scale factor would be 0.25.

b. Changing the location of the center of dilation changes only the location of the image; it does not change the dimensions of the image.

c. Sample response: The image is larger than the original if the scale factor is greater than 1.

d. Reflections, rotations, and translations are isometries because congruence is preserved. Although the measures of angles and the ratios between adjacent sides are preserved under dilations, they are not necessarily isometries. The preimage and image are congruent under a dilation only if the scale factor is 1.

Teacher Note

To complete Problems **3.1** and **3.2**, students will need copies of templates G and H. Blackline masters appear at the end of this teacher edition.

Assignment

***3.1** Sample response:

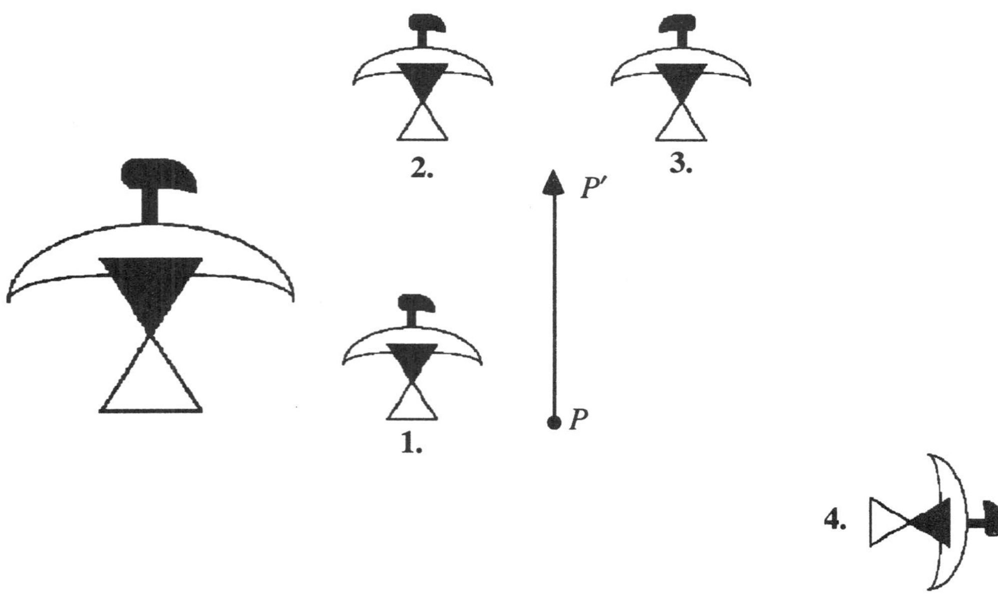

***3.2** **a.** The line of reflection can be found by constructing the perpendicular bisector of a segment whose endpoints are corresponding points on the image and preimage (or by paper folding).

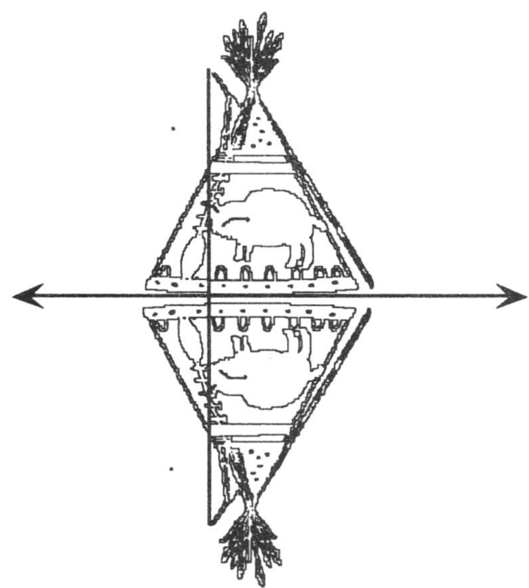

b. The center of rotation can be found by determining the perpendicular bisectors of two segments whose endpoints are corresponding points on the image and preimage. The intersection of the perpendicular bisectors is the center of rotation.

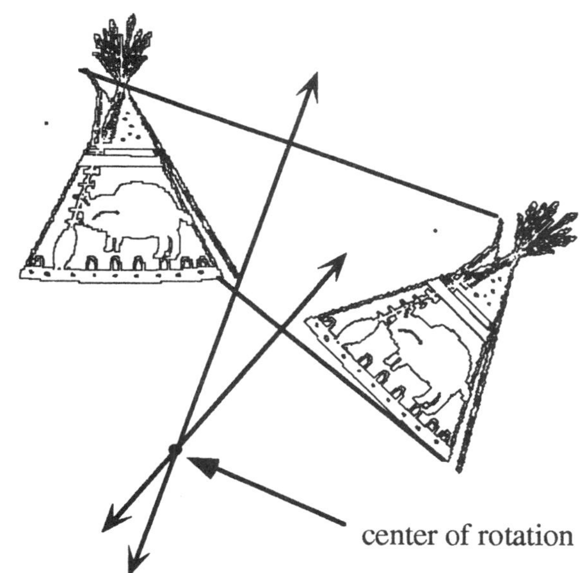

c. The vector may be indicated by connecting any point and its image, in the direction from the preimage to the image.

d. The center of dilation can be found at the intersection of two lines connecting corresponding points on the image and preimage. The scale factor is approximately 2.

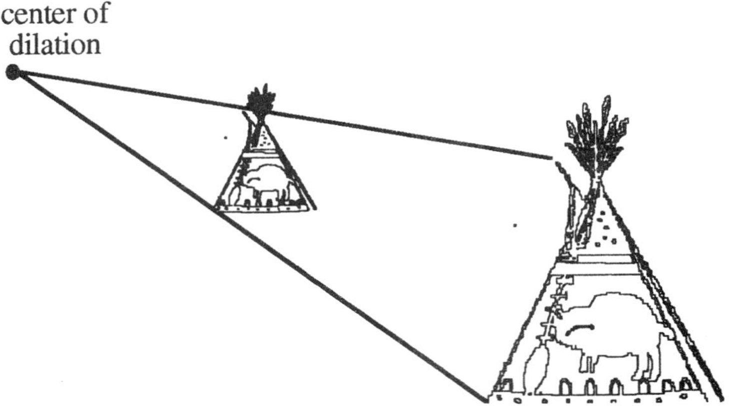

e. Two possible reflection lines are perpendicular to a line connecting any point and its image. The distance between the reflection lines is half the distance between the point and its image.

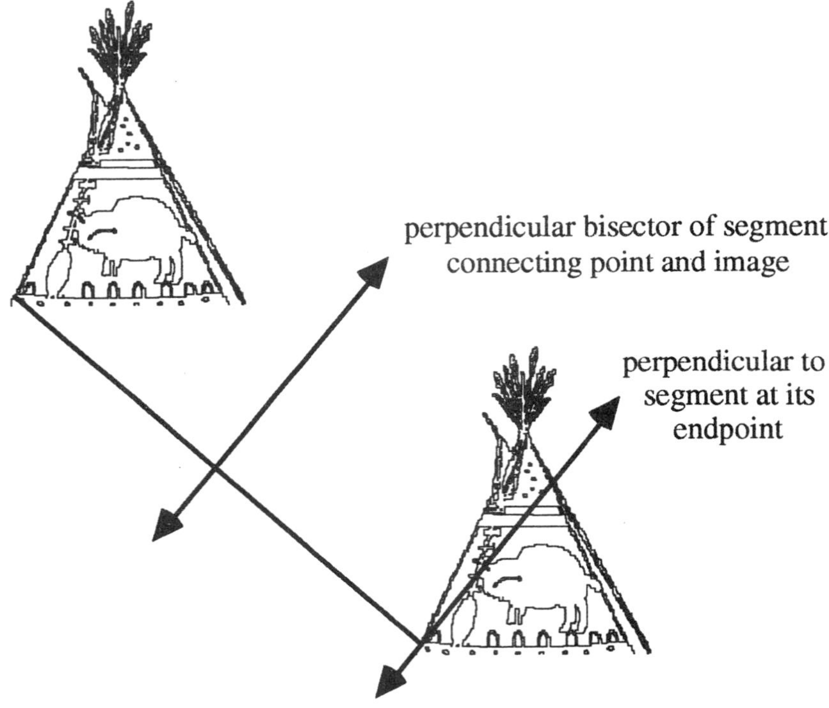

3.3 **a.** To help students consider possible designs, you may wish to provide some reference materials.

b. You may prefer to ask students to give oral presentations.

* * * * *

Research Project

Students have many choices for both culture and historical period. Besides the examples listed in the student edition, several movements in modern and contemporary art make dramatic use of geometric shapes and lines.

3.4 The following table provides sample descriptions for each figure.

Figure	Description of Transformation
2.	Not an isometry and not similar. Not an obvious type of transformation.
3.	Not an isometry, but similar. Dilation using *C* as the center. Scale factor appears to be 0.5.
4.	Not an isometry, but similar. Dilation using *A* as the center. Scale factor appears to be 3.
5.	An isometry and therefore also similar. A translation by a vector equivalent to the vector from *F* to *G*, with a length of approximately 4.3 cm, in a direction which can described as about 300°, or a bearing of about 150°, or approximately southeast.
6.	Not an isometry, but similar. Two transformations: first a dilation identical to figure 3, then a reflection in the line containing $\overline{DE}$.
7.	An isometry and therefore also similar. A rotation of 90° about point *B*.
8.	Not an isometry and not similar. Not an obvious type of transformation.

Answers to Summary Assessment

1. **a.** Sample response: Parallel lines could be cut as shown in the sketch below. The resulting strips can be shifted one color and re-sewn.

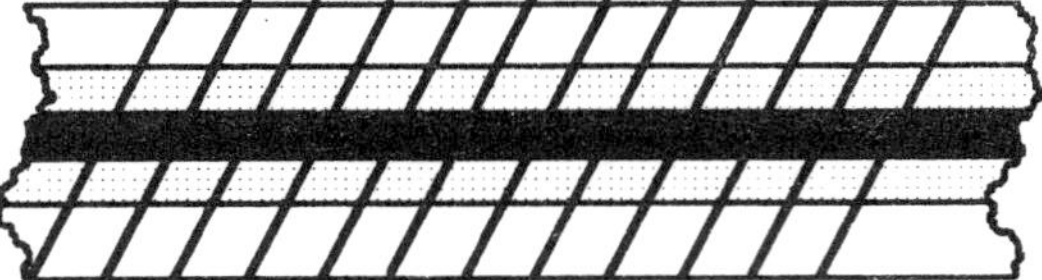

   b. Answers will vary. Cutting the fabric along parallel lines creates congruent corresponding angles. Re-aligning the new strips along the parallels creates the pattern of parallelograms.

2. **a–b.** Sample sketch:

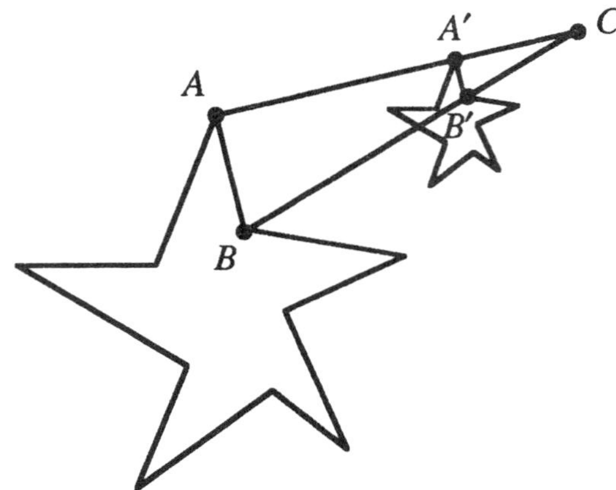

   c. The following sample response refers to the labeled points in the diagram above: Since the transformation is a dilation, $\Delta ABC \sim \Delta A'B'C$. Therefore, $\angle BAC \cong \angle B'A'C$. Since these are corresponding angles, $\overline{AB}$ is parallel to $\overline{A'B'}$. A similar argument could be used for every pair of corresponding sides.

3. a. The center of rotation can be found by constructing the perpendicular bisectors of segments connecting corresponding points on the image and preimage, as shown below.

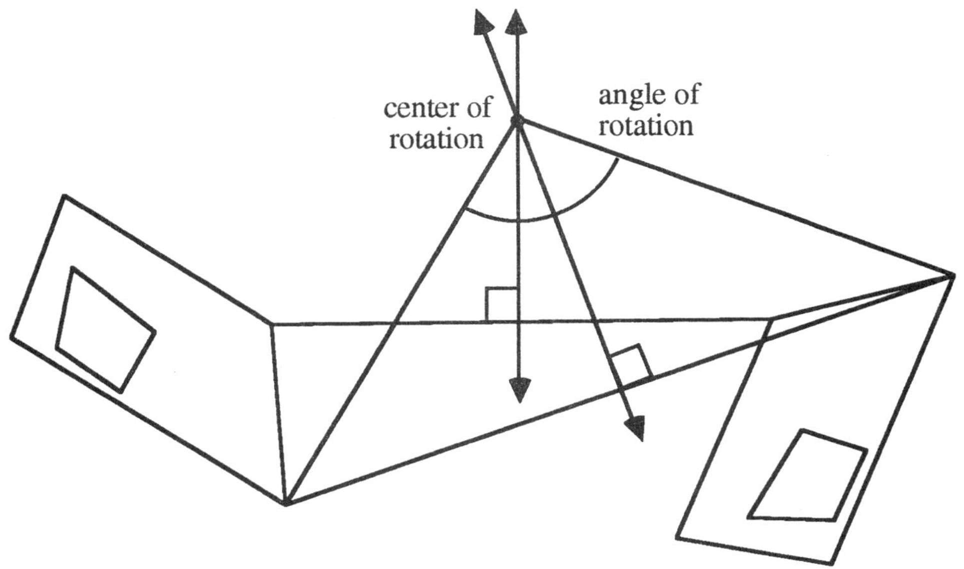

b. Sample sketch:

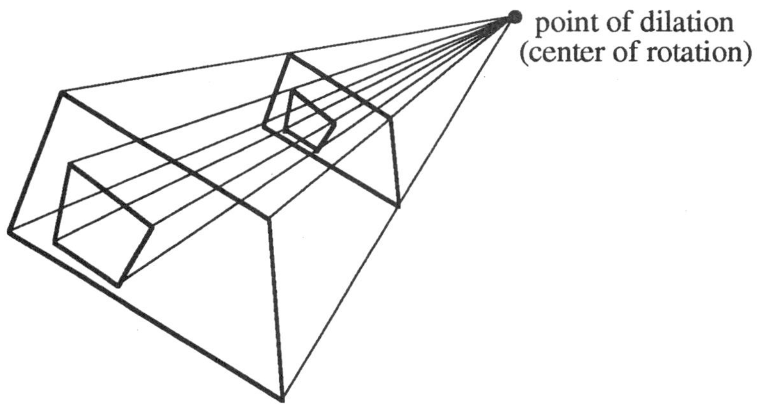

Teacher Note

To complete Problem **3** in the module assessment, each student will need one copy of template I.

Module Assessment

1. In the diagram below, line x is parallel to line y. Find the measure of each labeled angle.

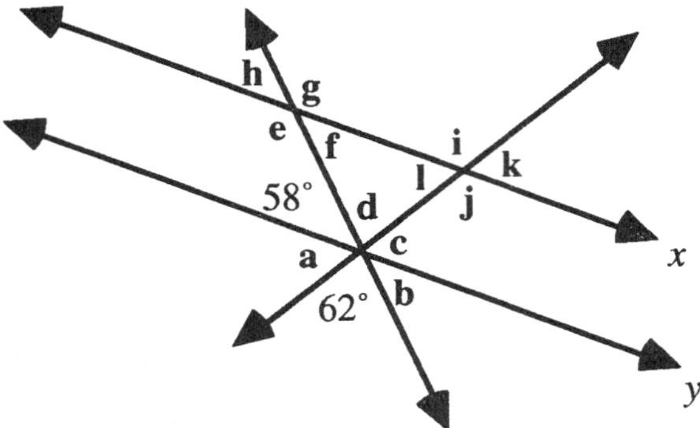

2. Find the center of the circle below. In a paragraph, describe the procedure that you used.

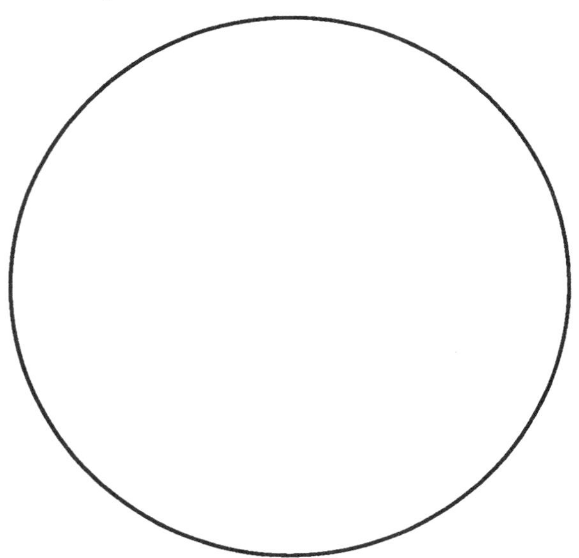

3. The crossed arrows in the diagram below symbolize friendship in some traditional American Indian artworks.

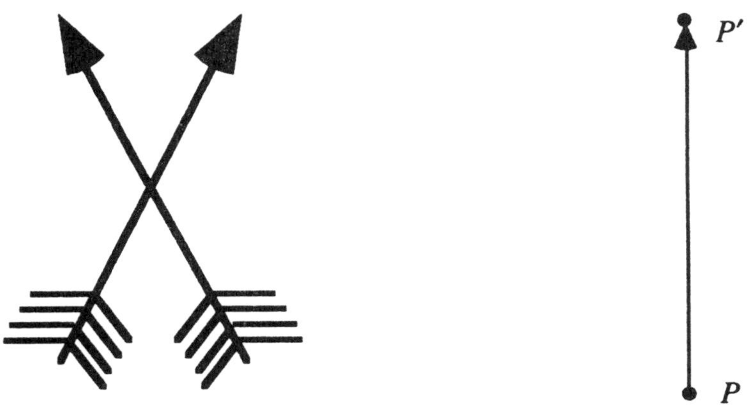

Use a copy of this diagram to complete the following transformations.

a. a dilation with center at point P and a scale factor of 1/4

b. a translation of the image found in Part **a** using the vector PP'

c. a reflection of the image found in Part **b** in a line containing P and P'.

d. a 45° clockwise rotation of the image found in Part **c** about point P

Answers to Module Assessment

1.
- **a.** 60°
- **b.** 58°
- **c.** 60°
- **d.** 62°
- **e.** 122°
- **f.** 58°
- **g.** 122°
- **h.** 58°
- **i.** 120°
- **j.** 120°
- **k.** 60°
- **l.** 60°

2. The center of the circle can be found by constructing the perpendicular bisectors of any two chords. The intersection of these chords is the center of the circle.

3. Sample sketch:

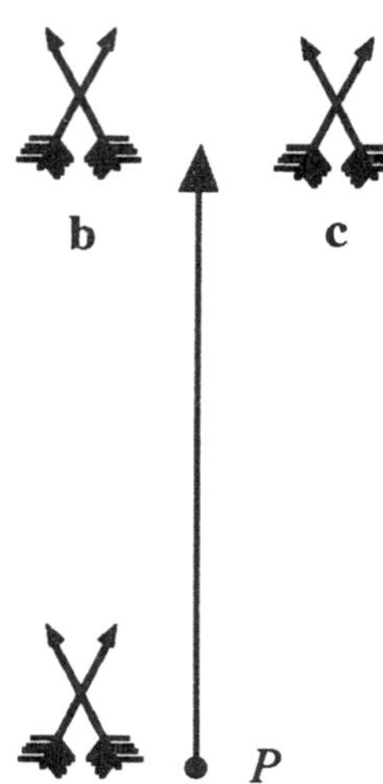

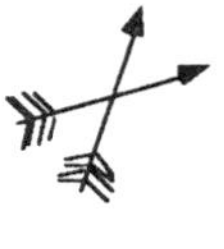

Selected References

Better Homes and Gardens. *American Patchwork and Quilting*. Des Moines, IA: Meredith Corporation, 1985.

Bradkin, C. G. *The Seminole Patchwork Book.* Westminster, CA: Yours Truly Inc., 1980.

Britton, J., F. Lindstrom, V. Ochiro, and W. Peterson. "Medicine Wheels: the Art and Culture of the Plains Indian." Seattle, WA: Seattle Public Schools, 1983. ERIC ED 45 849.

Brown, P. "Native Americans: An Elementary Art Unit." Washington, DC: U.S. Department of Education, 1978. ERIC ED 241 417.

Cordova, D. "The Navajo Way of Life: A Resource Unit with Activities for Grades 4–6." Salt Lake City, UT: Salt Lake City School District, 1982. ERIC ED 235 962.

Gale, N. "Strong Tribal Identity Can Protect Native American Youth. How Can We Help?" Washington, DC: Native American Development Corporation, 1985. ERIC ED 329 391.

Lafarge, O. *A Pictorial History of the American Indian*. New York: Crown Publishers, 1956.

Nabakov, P., and R. Easten. *Native American Architecture*. New York: Oxford University Press, 1989.

Olson, A. T. *Mathematics Through Paper Folding*. Reston, VA: National Council of Teachers of Mathematics, 1972.

Storm, H. *Seven Arrows.* New York: Ballantine Books, 1972.

Flashbacks

Activity 1

1.1 Use the parallelogram in the diagram below to complete Parts **a–e**.

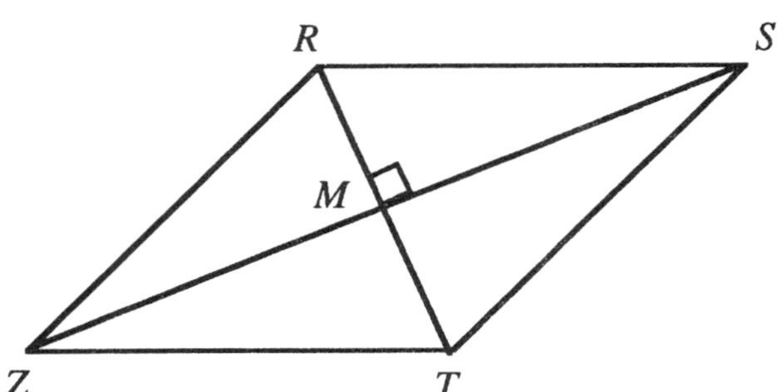

a. Name the interior angles of the parallelogram that are adjacent to $\angle SRZ$.

b. Name the interior angle of the parallelogram that is opposite $\angle SRZ$.

c. If $\angle RZM \cong \angle TZM$, then $\overline{ZS}$ is called an _________.

d. If $\overline{RM} \cong \overline{TM}$, then $\overline{ZS}$ is called a _________.

e. Identify a line of symmetry for the parallelogram.

Activity 2

2.1 Using the figure below as the preimage, sketch its image for each transformation listed in Parts **a–d**.

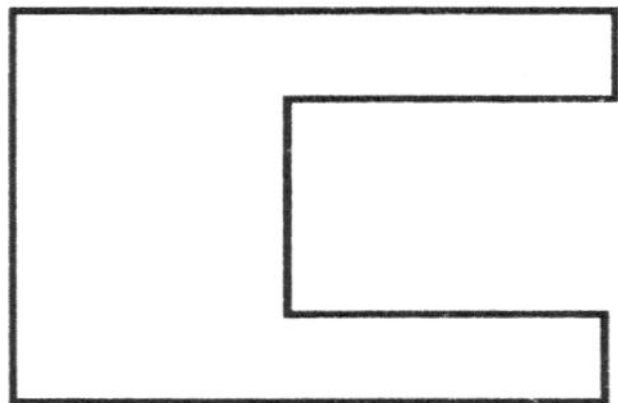

a. a reflection

b. a rotation

c. a dilation

d. a translation

2.2 **a.** Draw a triangle *ABC* inscribed in a circle.

b. Draw a circle inscribed in a triangle *ABC*.

Activity 3

3.1 When are two objects similar?

3.2 Find the value of x in each of the following proportions.

a. $\frac{3}{x} = \frac{6}{10}$

b. $\frac{5}{6} = \frac{x}{36}$

3.3 Consider the two similar triangles below.

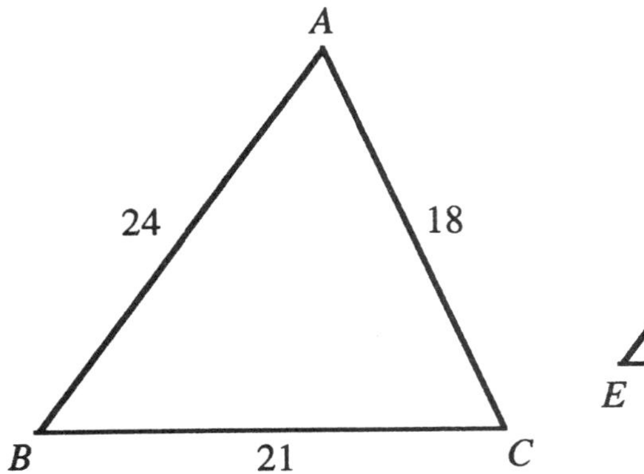

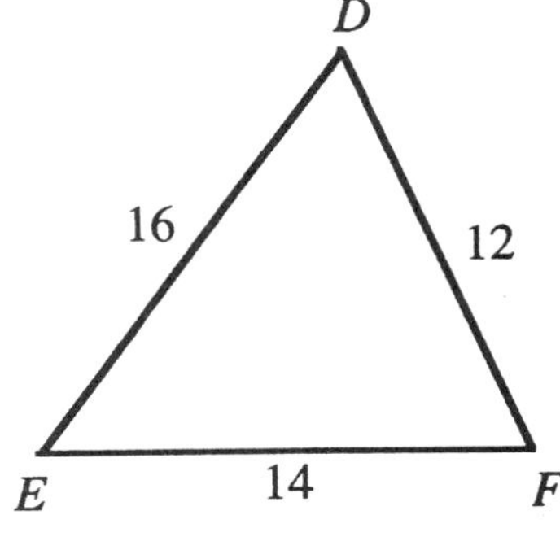

a. What is the value of the scale factor that creates triangle *DEF* from triangle *ABC*?

b. What is the value of the scale factor that creates triangle *ABC* from triangle *DEF*?

Answers to Flashbacks

Activity 1

1.1

a. $\angle RST$ and $\angle TZR$

b. $\angle ZTS$

c. angle bisector

d. perpendicular bisector

e. line SZ or line RT

Activity 2

2.1 The diagram below shows a sample response for each transformation.

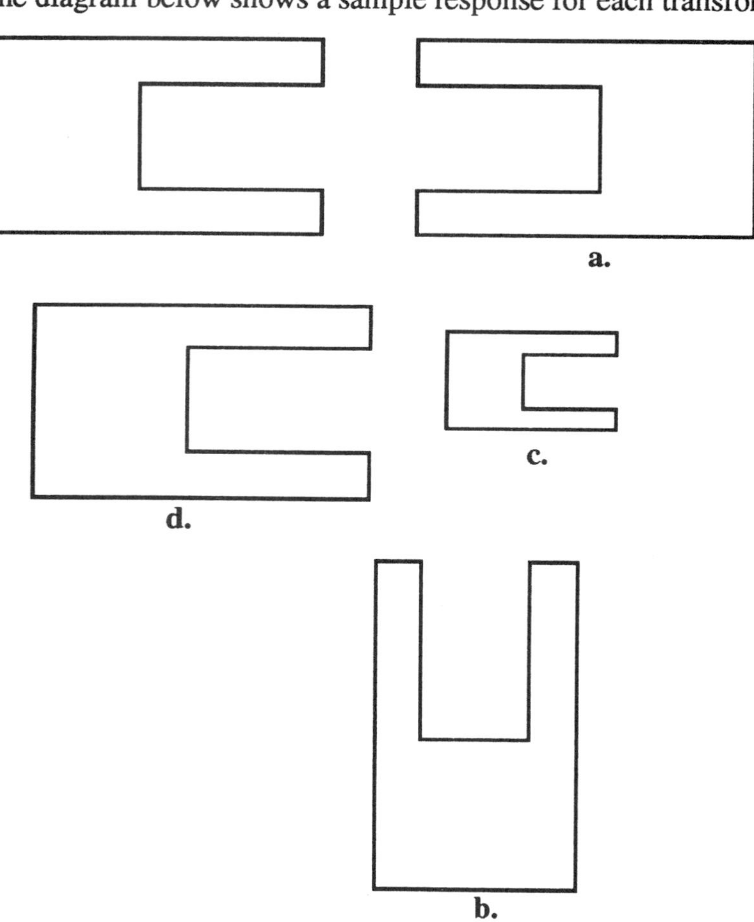

2.2 Sample sketches:

a.

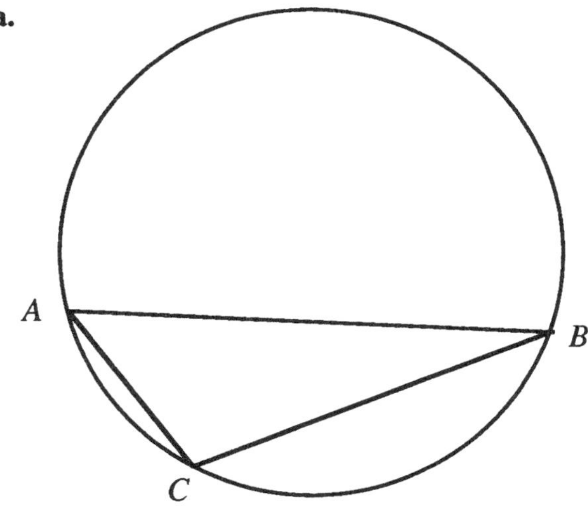

b.

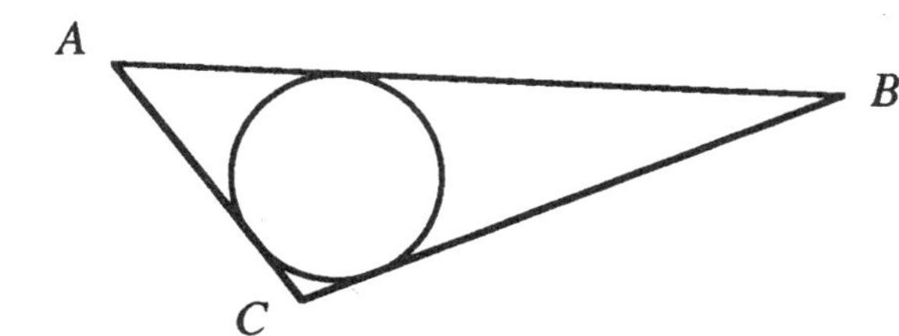

Activity 3

3.1 Sample response: Two objects are similar if the measures of corresponding angles are equal and the lengths of corresponding sides are proportional.

3.2 **a.** $x = 5$

b. $x = 30$

3.3 **a.** 2/3

c. 3/2

Template A

Template B

Template C

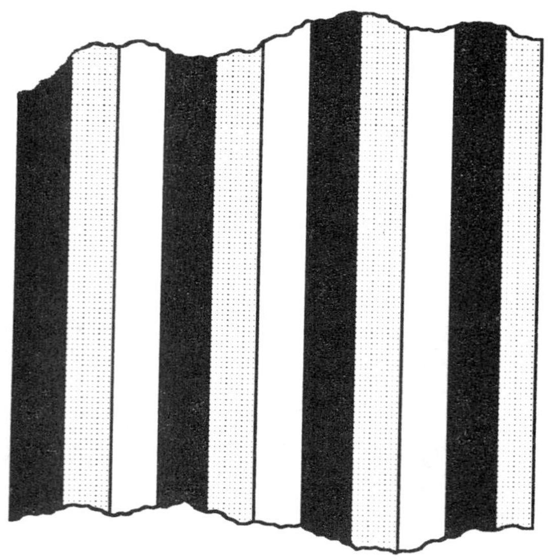

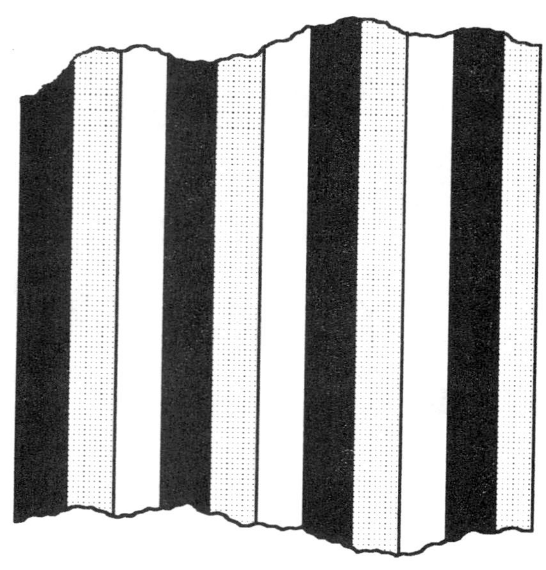

Template D

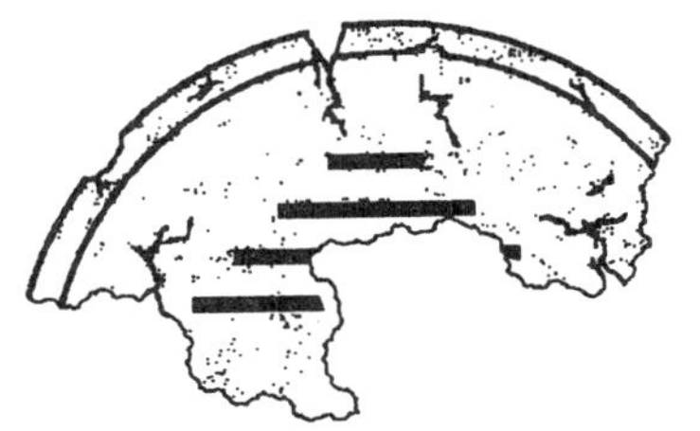

Template E

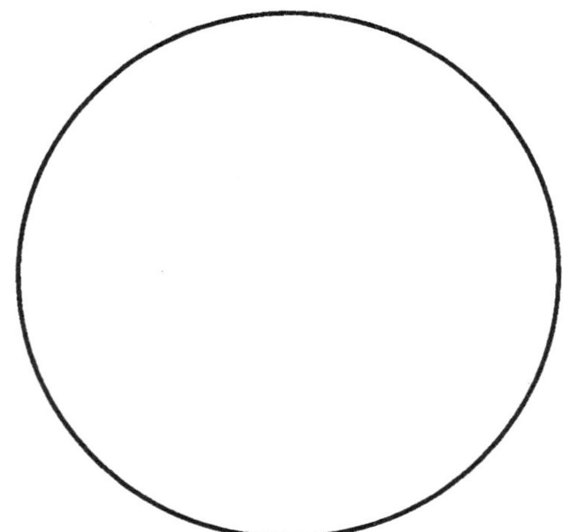

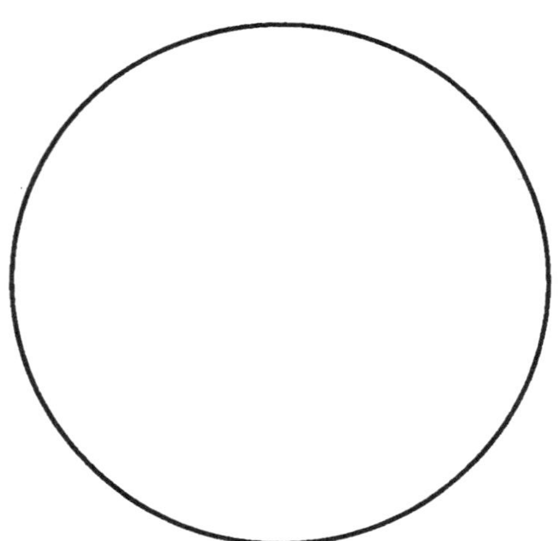

Template F

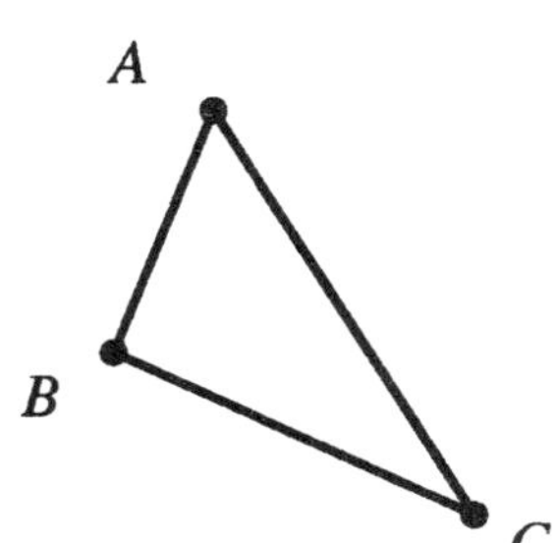

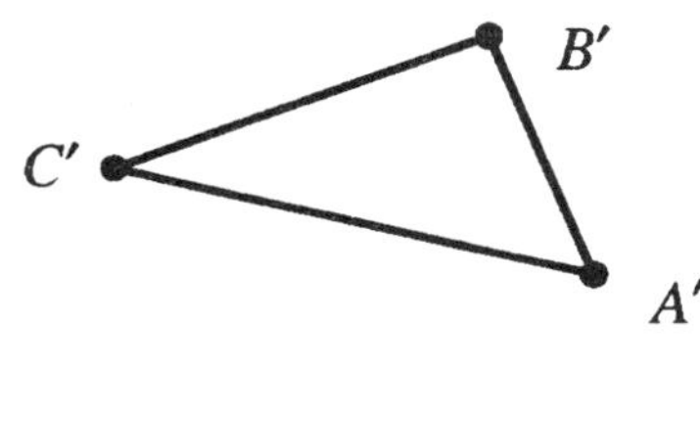

Template G

Template H

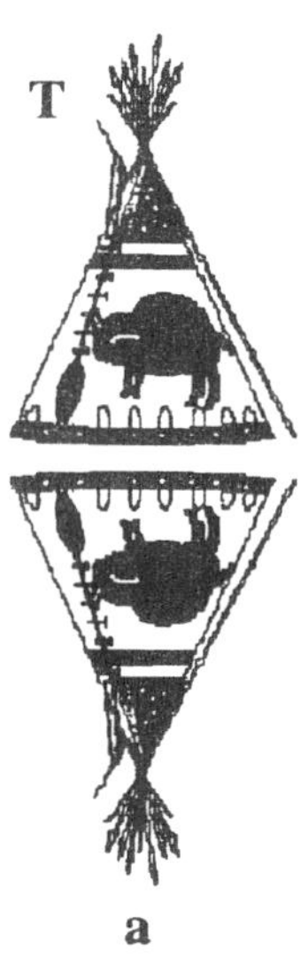

a

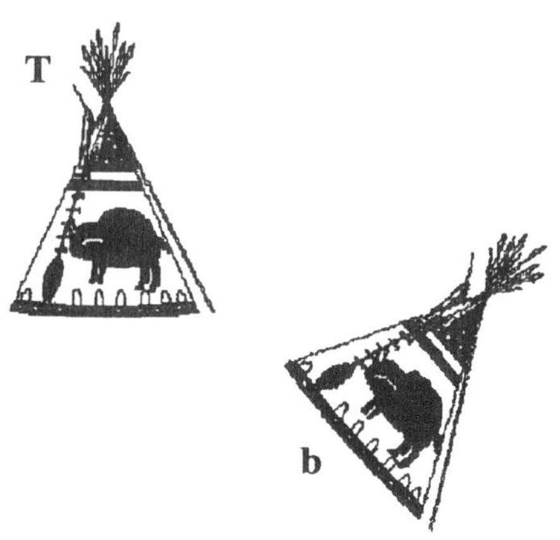

b

Template H (continued)

c

d

Template I

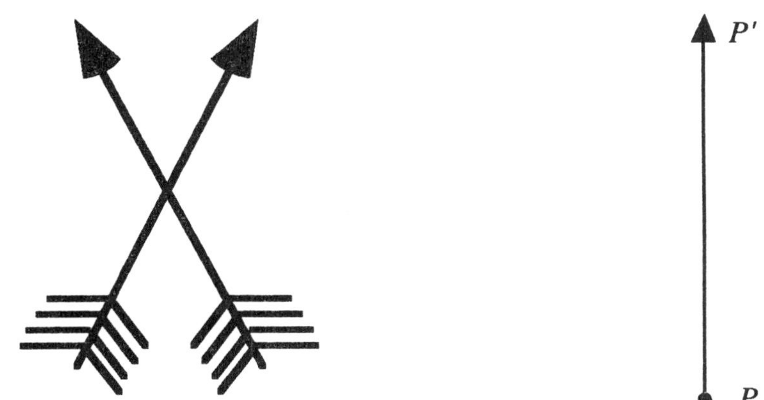

If the Shoe Fits . . .

How can you tell when two quantities—like age and heart rate—are related? In this module, you explore methods for finding and evaluating mathematical models of some important relationships.

Byron Anderson • Ruth Brocklebank • Pete Stabio

Teacher Edition

If the Shoe Fits . . .

Overview

In this module, students explore methods of determining linear models for sets of data. Using data from exercise physiology, students are introduced to median-median lines and regression lines. They also use residual plots to evaluate models.

Objectives

In this module, students will:

- use the sum of the absolute values of the residuals to compare how well linear models fit a set of data
- model data using the median-median line
- use the least-squares method to find a linear regression equation
- graph and analyze residual plots.

Prerequisites

For this module, students should know:

- how to identify graphs with positive or negative associations
- how to create scatterplots
- how to calculate residuals
- how to determine the equation of a line in the form $y = mx + b$
- how to determine the median of a set of data.

Time Line

Activity	1	2	3	Summary Assessment	Total
Days	2	3	2	1	8

Materials Required

Materials	Activity			
	1	2	3	Summary Assessment
graph paper	X	X	X	
straightedge	X	X	X	
meterstick or measuring tape		X		

Technology

Software	Activity			
	1	2	3	Summary Assessment
graphing utility	X	X	X	X
spreadsheet	X	X	X	X

If the Shoe Fits...

Introduction

The module uses data from human physiology to introduce relationships that may be modeled mathematically.

Discussion

a. If the employee is paid by the hour, there is a positive association, since the more the employee works, the more the employee earns. If the employee is not paid by the hour, there may be no relationship, since earnings are the same regardless of the number of hours worked.

b. Sample response: Since the taller players on the team typically play the forward positions and one of the main objectives of forwards is to score, there may be a positive association between height and the number of points scored. However, individual scoring depends on many factors other than height, so there may not always be a relationship.

c. Unless students are subject to certain travel restrictions, no relationship is likely. However, there is probably a positive association between the distance a student travels and the amount of time it takes the student to arrive at school.

d. The relationship between these two quantities is examined in later activities. Accidents are more likely for younger, novice drivers. They also become more likely for elderly drivers.

e. Sample response: Since students with high GPAs usually study, there may be a positive association between the number of hours spent studying and a student's GPA. However, a student's GPA may depend on many factors other than studying, so there may not always be a relationship.

Activity 1

In this activity, students find linear models for a set of data, determine the equations of their models, then calculate the sum of the absolute values of the residuals. **Note:** Students will examine the least-squares method in Activity **3**. Both the sum of the absolute values of the residuals and the sum of the squares of the residuals are reasonable measures of how well a model fits the data. Developed by Carl Friedrich Gauss (1777–1855), the method of least squares is preferred by mathematicians.

Materials List

- straightedge (one per student)
- graph paper (one sheet per student)

Technology

- spreadsheet
- graphing utility

Exploration

Students fit lines to a set of data, then determine the equations of these lines. To evaluate their models, students calculate the sum of the absolute values of the residuals.

a. Sample scatterplot and line:

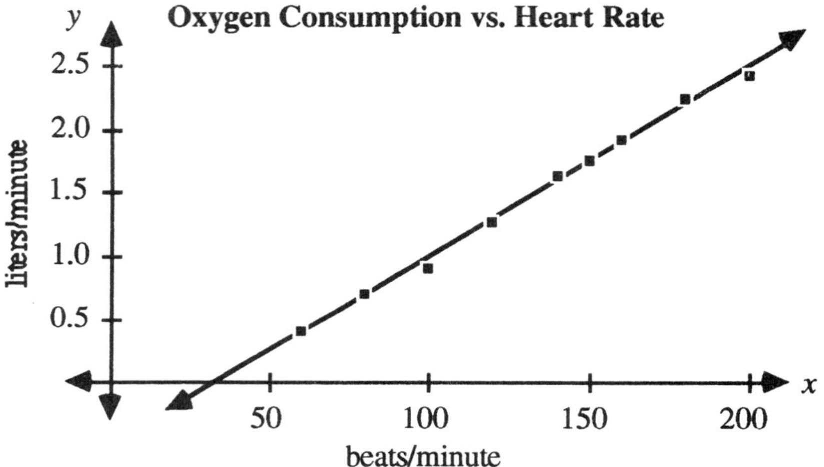

b. The equation of the sample line shown in Part **a** is $y = 0.015x - 0.470$.

c. Answers will vary, depending on the line. The following table shows the sum of the squares of the residuals using the equation $y = 0.015x - 0.470$.

x	y	**predicted** y	**|residual|**
60	0.41	0.43	0.02
80	0.71	0.73	0.02
100	0.90	1.03	0.13
120	1.27	1.33	0.06
140	1.62	1.63	0.01
150	1.76	1.78	0.02
160	1.92	1.93	0.01
180	2.24	2.23	0.01
200	2.42	2.53	0.11
		Sum	0.39

d. Students try to reduce the sum of the absolute values of the residuals by adjusting the slope and y-intercept of the model equation. For example, the equation $y = 0.015x - 0.49$ results in a lower sum of 0.29.

Discussion

a. Students should observe that an increase in heart rate is associated with an increase in oxygen consumption. The relationship appears to be linear.

b. Answers may vary. Students may use residuals, sums of residuals, and visual criteria as justifications. Although a good model may not contain all the points of a scatterplot, it should approximate the general trend of the data.

c. Sample response: Yes, the line comes very close to most of the data points.

d.

1. The equation with the smallest sum of the absolute values of the residuals should have a slope of approximately 0.015 and a y-intercept of approximately –0.49.
2. Answers may vary. Some students may have adjusted either the slope or y-intercept, while others may have adjusted both.

e.

1. Students may suggest determining an estimate from the graph of the line or using the equation to calculate the y-value when $x = 168$.
2. Students may suggest determining an estimate from the graph of the line or using the equation to calculate the x-value when $y = 1.5$.

f. Answers will vary. Sample response: It is often dangerous to make predictions for values outside the observed data. For example, the domain and range of the model may be restricted in the real-world setting.

Teacher Note

In the following assignment, students are asked to find linear models for data sets. For the sake of comparison, the sample responses given include the linear regression equation for each data set. Students will examine linear regression models in Activity **3**. They are not expected to use these models in this assignment.

Assignment

1.1 **a.** Sample scatterplot:

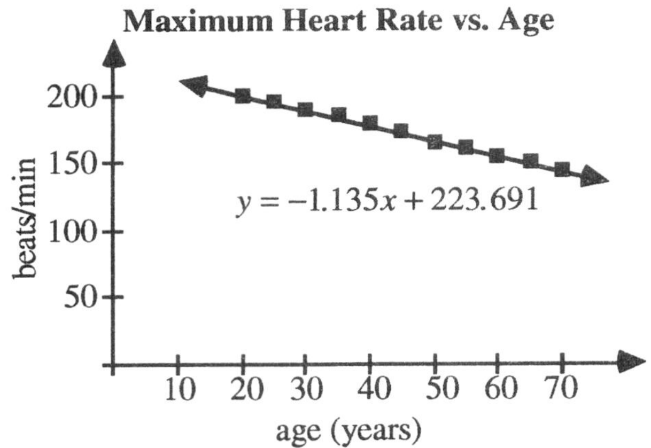

b. Answers will vary. **Note:** The linear regression equation for this data is $y = -1.135x + 223.691$.

c. Answers will vary, depending on the equation from Part **b**. Using the equation $y = -1.135x + 223.691$, the sum of the absolute values of the residuals is approximately 8.434.

d. Using the equation $y = -1.135x + 223.691$, the suggested maximum heart rate for a person of age 15 would be about 207 beats/min.

e. Sample response: Using the linear model, the suggested maximum heart rate at age 3 is about 220 beats/min. This is the upper limit for the human heart. Therefore, it would probably be wise to use a different model for small children.

***1.2** **a.** Sample scatterplot:

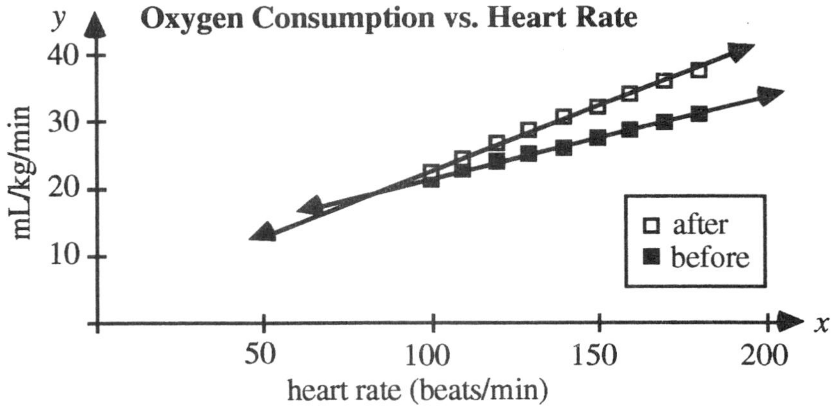

b. Answers may vary. A possible equation for the "after" data is $y = 0.186x + 4.128$, while a possible equation for the "before" data is $y = 0.12x + 9.403$.

c. Answers may vary. Using the equations from Part **b**, the model for the "before" data has a sum of the absolute values of the residuals of approximately 0.637, while the model for the "after" data has a sum of approximately 1.517. Therefore, the model for the "before" data appears to provide a better fit.

d. Using the sample equations from Part **b**, the predicted heart rate before an aerobic conditioning program is about 255 beats/min, while the predicted heart rate after an aerobic conditioning program is about 193 beats/min.

* * * * *

Teacher Note

In Problems **1.3** and **1.4** (and again in Activities **2** and **3**), the sample responses use $x = 0$ for the initial year. In Problem **1.3**, for example, the first data point is (0,1049) rather than (1984,1049). Students may choose to use the actual year. You may wish to point out that, for a linear model, the slope is the same in either case, although the y-intercept is different.

***1.3** **a.** Sample scatterplot:

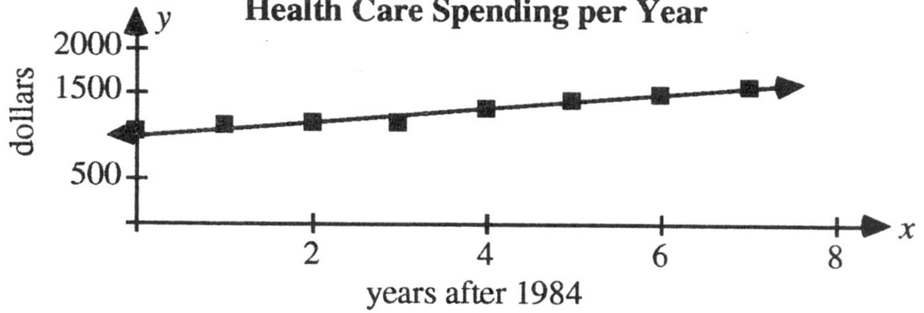

b. Answers will vary. **Note:** The equation of the regression line for this data is $y = 75.881x + 1005.167$. A graph of this equation is shown on the scatterplot in Part **a**.

c. Using the equation from Part **b**, the sum of the absolute values of the residuals is approximately 260.9.

d. Using the equation from Part **b**, the predicted mean amount, per person, is approximately $2219.

1.4 **a.** Sample scatterplot:

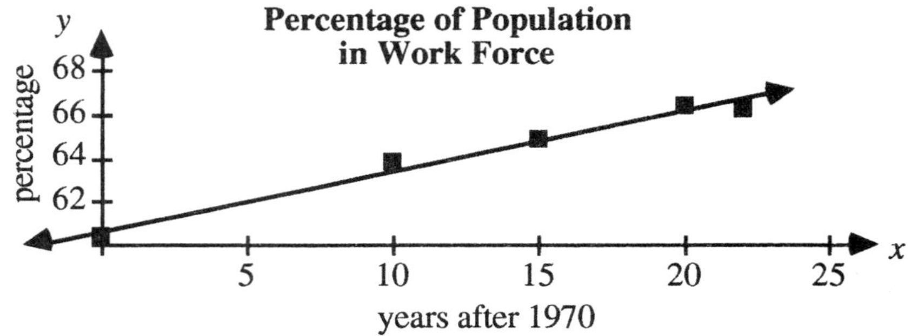

b. Answers will vary. **Note:** The equation of the regression line for this data is $y = 0.276x + 60.645$.

c. Using the equation from Part **b**, approximately 68.9% of the population will participate in the work force in the year 2000.

d. Answers will vary. The sample prediction in Part **c** is only 0.2% higher than the prediction made by the Bureau of the Census.

* * * * * * * * * *

Activity 2

Students explore the median-median line as a tool for modeling linear data.

Materials List

- straightedge (one per student)
- graph paper (one sheet per student)
- meterstick or measuring tape (one per pair of students)

Technology

- spreadsheet
- graphing utility

Exploration

Students model the relationship between arm span and shoe size using a median-median line. **Note:** The differences between male and female shoe sizes appear to have little effect on the results of this exploration.

a. The sample data shown in the following table was gathered from a class of 32 students consisting of 17 girls and 15 boys.

Shoe Size	Arm Span (cm)	Shoe Size	Arm Span (cm)
7.5	157	9	173
7.5	165	9	180
7.5	168	9.5	178
7.5	168	9.5	178
8	160	9.5	180
8	165	9.5	183
8	168	10	173
8	170	10	178
8.5	163	10	178
8.5	165	10	183
8.5	175	11	183
8.5	178	11	185
9	165	11.5	183
9	165	12	183
9	168	12	185
9	170	13	188

b. A scatterplot of the sample data is shown below.

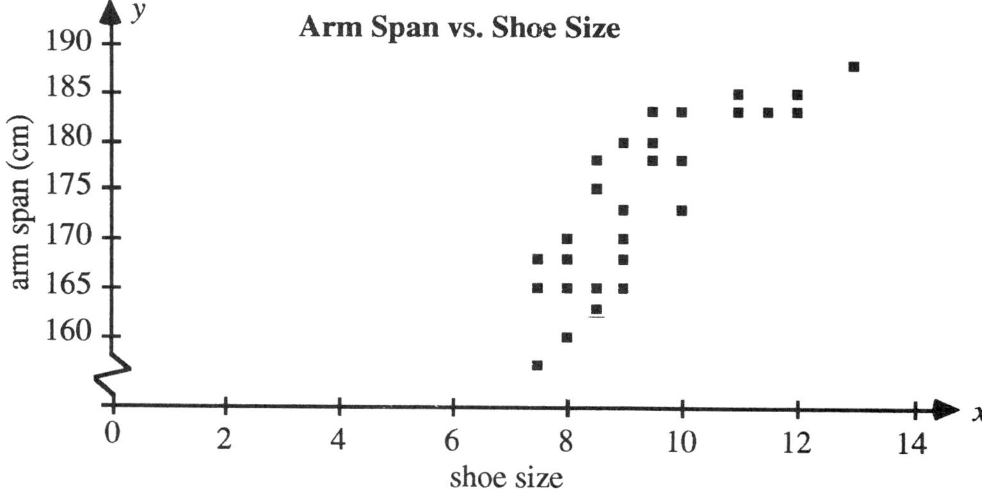

c. The following table divides the sample data into three groups.

First Group		Middle Group		Third Group	
Shoe Size	Arm Span (cm)	Shoe Size	Arm Span (cm)	Shoe Size	Arm Span (cm)
7.5	157	9	165	10	173
7.5	165	9	165	10	178
7.5	168	9	168	10	178
7.5	168	9	170	10	183
8	160	9	173	11	183
8	165	9	180	11	185
8	168	9.5	178	11.5	183
8	170	9.5	178	12	183
8.5	163	9.5	180	12	185
8.5	165	9.5	183	13	188
8.5	175				
8.5	178				

d. The coordinates of the summary points for the sample data are (8,166.5), (9,175.5), and (11,183).

e.
1. Using the sample data given in Part **a**, the equation of the line determined by the first and third summary points is $y = 5.5x + 122.5$.
2. Substituting the x-coordinate of the middle summary point into the equation from Step **1** gives the y-coordinate of the corresponding point on the line. For the sample data, the coordinates of this point are (9,172).
3. Since the y-coordinate of the middle summary point is 175.5, the vertical distance between these points is $175.5 - 172 = 3.5$. The coordinates of the point that is 1/3 the distance from the line are approximately (9,173.2).
4. Students should observe that this line has the same slope as the line in Step **1**.
5. For the sample data, the equation of the median-median line is approximately $y = 5.5x + 123.7$.

Discussion

a. The median is considered a good representative value for a set of data. It does not require complicated calculations, and is not as affected by outliers as other measures of central tendency.

b. Sample response: The median-median line provides a reasonable model. Although it does not contain all the points of the scatterplot, it describes the general trend of the data.

c. Sample response: The y-intercepts of the two lines differ by 1/3 of the vertical distance between the summary point of the middle group and the line containing the first and third summary points.

d. 1. Answers will vary. Using the median-median line for the sample data, the predicted arm span is 206 cm.

2. Sample response: An arm span of 206 cm is about 6 ft, 9 in. This seems reasonable for someone who wears size 15 shoes.

Assignment

2.1 a. Answers will vary. Using the sample equation given in the exploration, Wadlow's predicted shoe size is 30.

b. The sample prediction is substantially low. Depending on student estimates, this question may illustrate the dangers of making predictions far outside the range of collected data.

2.2 a. Since students may have used estimated values during their calculations for the median-median line, their results may not exactly agree with those reported by technology.

b. Sample response: The two lines are very close. The equation of the median-median line found using technology does not take significant figures into account.

2.3 a. Sample scatterplot:

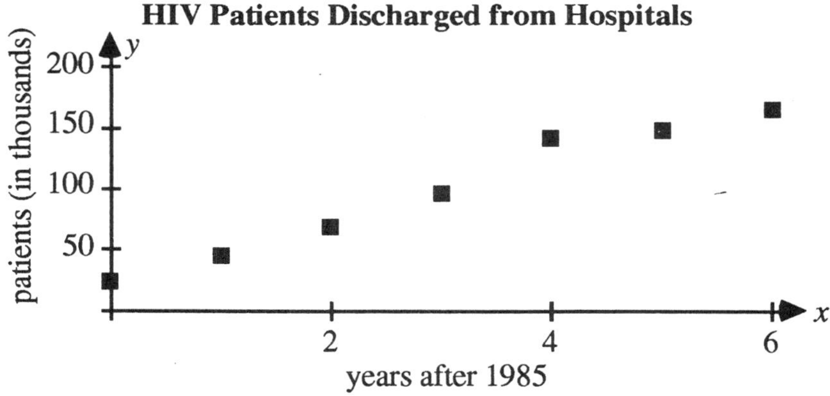

b. Using 1985 as $x = 0$, the equation of the median-median line is approximately $y = 24.4x + 21.5$.

c. Judging from the scatterplot, the number of HIV-positive patients discharged from hospitals appears to be increasing linearly.

* * * * *

2.4 **a.** Sample scatterplot:

b. Using 1970 as $x = 0$, the equation of the median-median line is approximately $y = 171x + 6663$.

c. **1.** Using the equation given in Part **b**, the estimated number of self-employed workers in 1988 is 9741.

2. The estimated value is less than 2% from the actual value.

2.5 **a.** Sample scatterplot:

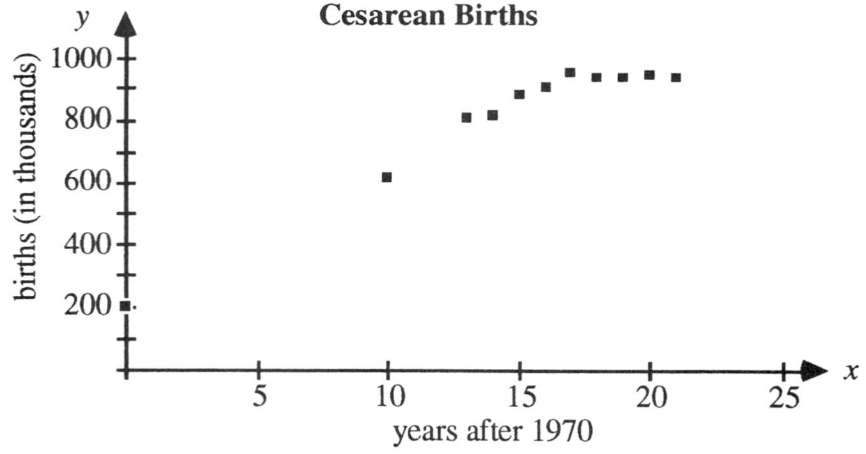

b. Using 1970 as $x = 0$, the equation of the median-median line is approximately $y = 27.8x + 417$.

c. Sample response: No, the median-median line does not appear to be a very good model of the data. Many of the data points are relatively far from the line.

d. Sample response: No. After 1987, the scatterplot appears to level off. In fact, from 1988 to 1991, the increase in the annual number of cesarean births was 0.

* * * * * * * * * *

Activity 3

In this activity, students determine linear regressions and evaluate linear models using residual plots. **Note:** The term *regression line* originated in statistical studies of the heights of children of tall parents because it described how those heights "regressed" toward the mean height of the population.

Materials List

- straightedge (one per student)
- graph paper (one sheet per student)

Technology

- spreadsheet
- graphing utility

Teacher Note

The least-squares method is used to generate equations for regression lines. The equations that students determine in Part **d** of Exploration **1** using a spreadsheet should approximate the linear regression.

Exploration 1

Students use the arm span and shoe size data from Activity **2** to examine a linear regression model. This equation is then compared to the median-median line found in Activity **2**.

a–b. Students recreate a scatterplot of the data for arm span vs. shoe size and determine the equation of a line that models the data reasonably well. (See sample graph in given in Part **b** of the exploration in Activity **2**.)

c–d. Students determine the sum of the squares of the residuals for their model. They then adjust the equation until they find the least sum.

For the sample data given in Activity **2**, the sum of the squares of the residuals for the regression line is approximately 718.2. In comparison, the sum of the squares of the residuals for the median-median line is about 795.1.)

e. Answers will vary. The linear regression equation for the sample data is $y = 4.8x + 129.1$.

Discussion 1

a.

1. Depending on the spread of the data, the median-median line may or may not be close to the linear regression.
2. Students should find that the two equations are quite similar.

b.

1. Sample response: The two models would differ greatly when there are outliers in the data. The median-median line only takes into account the median of each group of data, while the linear regression considers the residuals of all data points. Therefore, the median-median line would tend to reflect only the pattern of the "middle" points.
2. Sample response: The two models would be approximately the same when the data is grouped relatively tightly about the middle data points.

c. Sample response: The linear regression would be better when you wish to consider all the data collected in your interpretation or predictions. **Note:** It should be pointed out to students that statisticians prefer the linear regression model.

Exploration 2

Students investigate the use of residual plots as a tool for evaluating the appropriateness of a model.

a. Sample graph:

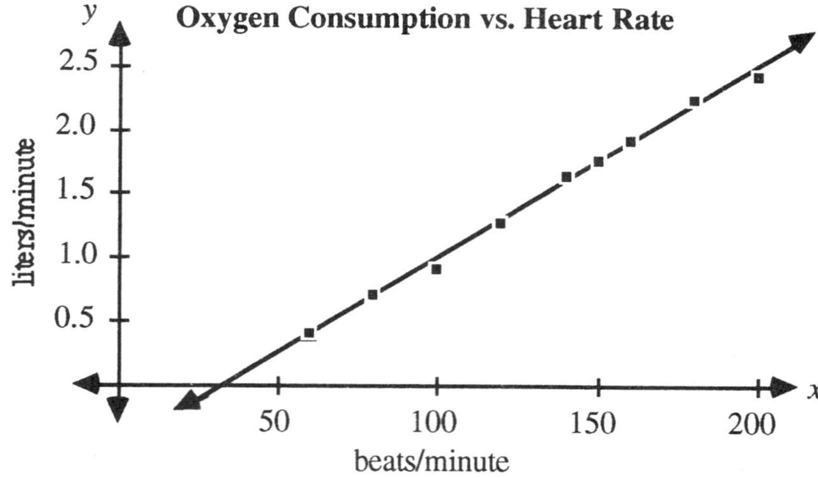

b. A completed table is shown below.

Heart Rate (beats/min)	Oxygen Consumption (L/min)	Predicted Oxygen Consumption	Residual
60	0.41	0.391	0.019
80	0.71	0.691	0.019
100	0.90	0.991	–0.091
120	1.27	1.291	–0.021
140	1.62	1.591	0.029
150	1.76	1.741	0.019
160	1.92	1.891	0.029
180	2.24	2.191	0.049
200	2.42	2.491	–0.071

c. The line $y = 0.015x - 0.509$ models the data well, as shown by the graph in Part **a**.

d. As shown in the following residual plot, the residuals appear to be scattered randomly above and below the x-axis.

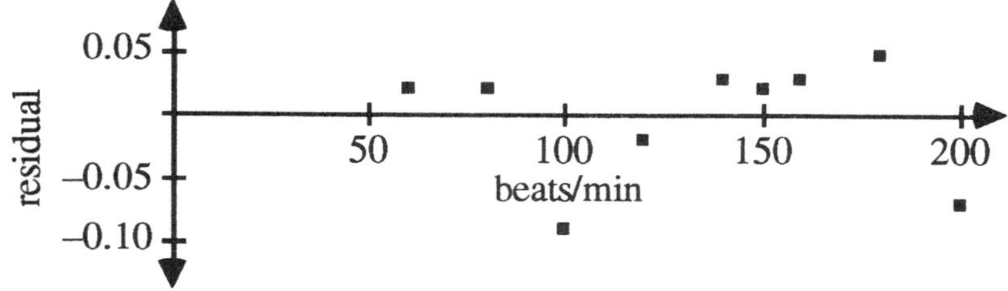

e. The following graph shows a scatterplot of the data in Table **5** along with the line $y = 0.02x - 1$.

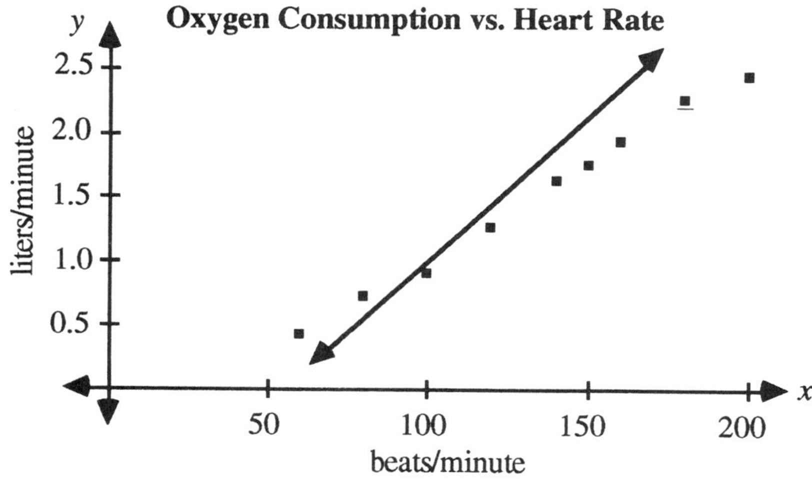

The table below shows the residuals that result using the model $y = 0.02x - 1$.

Heart Rate (beats/min)	Oxygen Consumption (L/min)	Predicted Oxygen Consumption	Residual
60	0.41	0.2	0.21
80	0.71	0.6	0.11
100	0.90	1	–0.1
120	1.27	1.4	–0.13
140	1.62	1.8	–0.18
150	1.76	2	–0.24
160	1.92	2.2	–0.28
180	2.24	2.6	–0.36
200	2.42	3	–0.58

The line $y = 0.02x - 1$ does not model the data well. As shown in the following residual plot, the residuals form a roughly linear pattern with a negative slope.

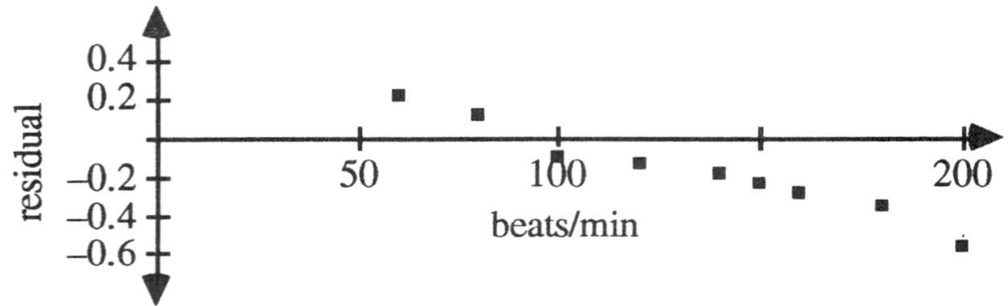

f. Students compare the residual plots for the two equations. In the residual plot for the better model, $y = 0.015x - 0.509$, the points are located closer to the x-axis and do not seem to form a recognizable pattern. **Note:** Although the equation $y = 0.02x - 1$ does not model the data well, the shape of the residual plot is linear. This indicates that a linear model is probably a good one for the data.

Discussion 2

a. Sample response: The equation $y = 0.015x - 0.509$ models the data better. A graph of this line is very close to most of the points on the scatterplot.

b. Sample response: If the points of a residual plot have no definite pattern and are distributed fairly evenly above and below the x-axis, the linear model is probably appropriate for the data.

c. 1. The points of this residual plot appear to have a linear pattern. Therefore, another linear model may provide a better fit for the data.

2. The points of this residual plot form a curved pattern. In this case, a linear model is probably not appropriate. **Note:** Some students may recognize the shape of the residual plot as a parabola and therefore suggest a quadratic model.

3. The points of this residual plot appear to have no definite pattern and are distributed fairly evenly above and below the x-axis.

4. The points of this residual plot appear to form an exponential curve. This suggests that an exponential model may be more appropriate.

Teacher Note

The use of some mathematical functions to model data involving time may be reasonable for relatively brief intervals, but may fail when applied to longer periods. For example, many relationships appear approximately linear only over short intervals. You may wish to point out the dangers of using such models to make predictions outside the range of the data.

Assignment

3.1 a. Sample scatterplot:

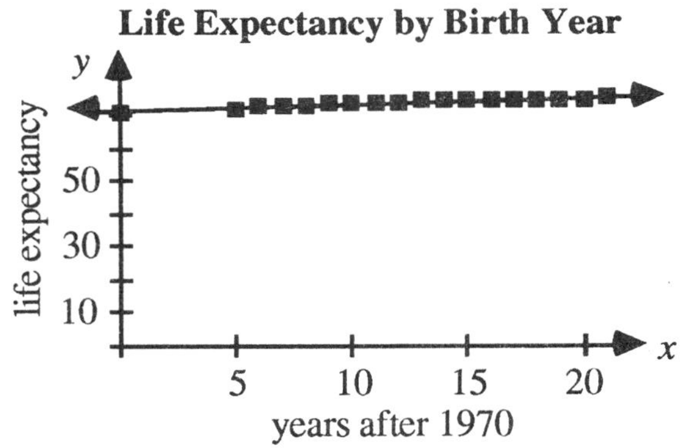

b. Using 1970 as $x = 0$, the equation of the regression line is $y = 0.197x + 71.698$.

c. Using the equation from Part **b**, the life expectancy of people born in 1973 is approximately 72.2 years; the life expectancy of people born in 2010 will be approximately 79.6 years.

d. The life expectancy from Part **c** is 2 years more than that predicted by the U.S. Census Bureau.

***3.2** **a.** The following graph shows a scatterplot of the data as well as the regression line $y = 1.129x - 0.655$.

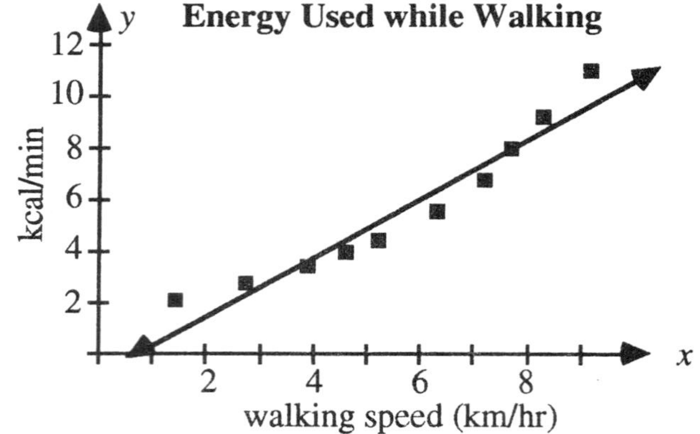

b. Sample residual plot:

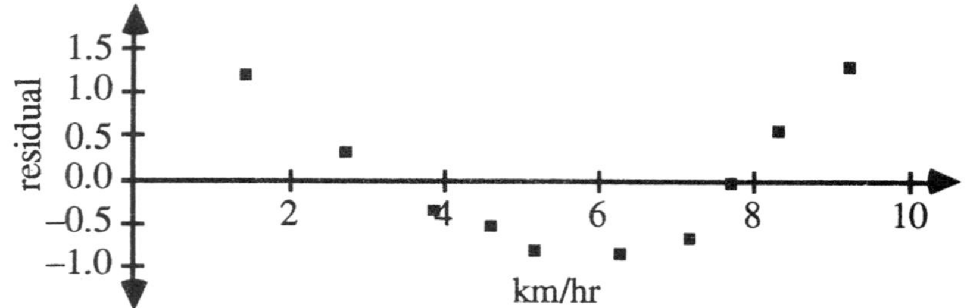

c. Sample response: The linear regression equation does not appear to be an appropriate model for the data. The shape of the scatterplot appears to be curved, not linear. In addition, the residual plot shows a definite pattern. **Note:** Some students may recognize the shape of the parabola.

***3.3** **a.** Using 1970 as $x = 0$, the equation of the regression line is $y = -0.939x + 83.937$.

b. Sample residual plot:

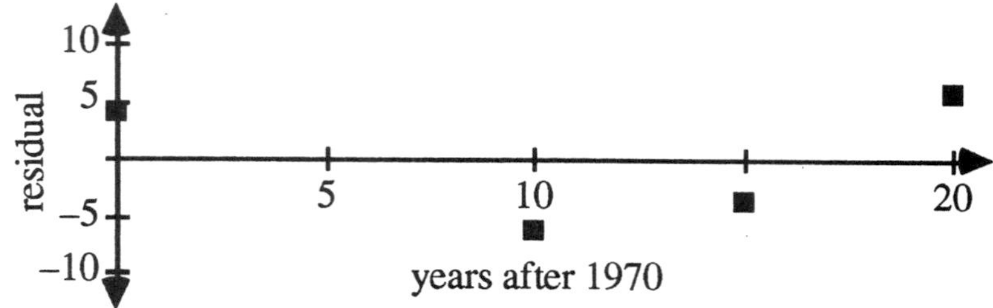

c. Sample response: There is probably a better model for the data than a line since the points of the residual plot appear to form a curve.

* * * * *

***3.4** **a.** Using 1984 as $x = 0$, the equation of the regression line is $y = 47.345x + 405.917$.

b. Using the equation from Part **a**, the predicted cost is about $1209.

c. Sample residual plot:

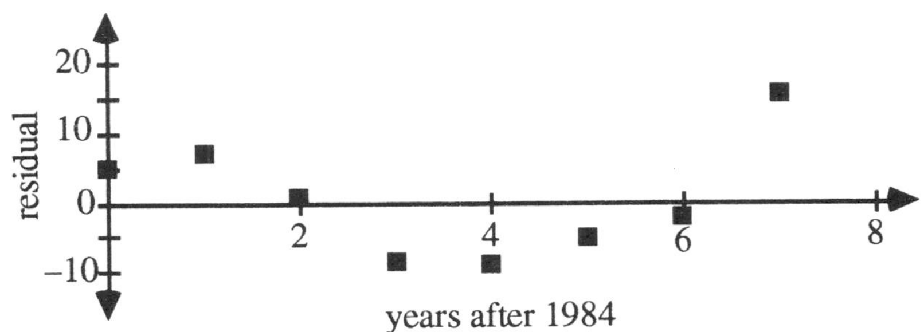

d. Sample response: There is probably a better model for the data than a line since the points of the residual plot appear to form a curve.

3.5 **a.** Using 1986 as $x = 0$, the equation of a regression line that models the data is $y = 1279.179x - 111{,}410.893$.

b. Using the equation in Part **a**, the average yearly increase in the American work force is approximately 1,279,000 men and women.

c. Sample residual plot:

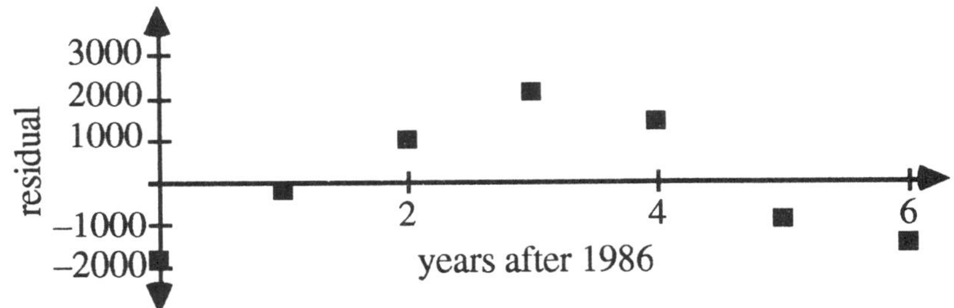

d. Sample response: Since the residual plot appears to show a pattern, a line is probably not an appropriate model for the data.

e. The equation of the regression line for the data for females is $y = 819.429x + 49587.286$. According to this model, the average yearly increase in the number of females in the American work force is approximately 819,000. Since the residual plot appears to show a pattern, a line is probably not an appropriate model for the data.

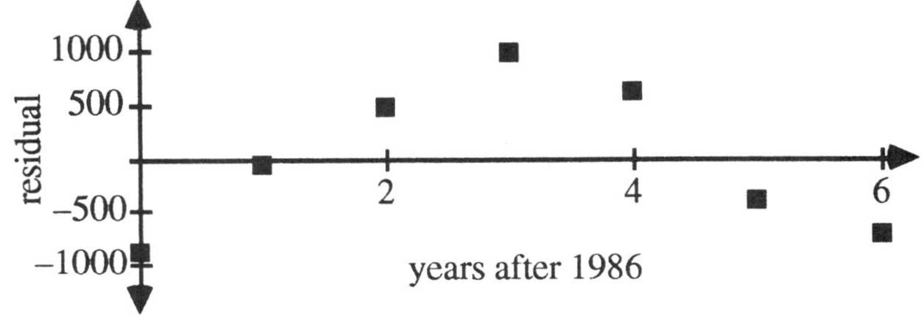

f. The equation of the regression line that models the data for males is $y = 459.75x + 61823.607$. According to this model, the average yearly increase in the number of males in the American work force is approximately 460,000. Since the residual plot appears to show a pattern, a line is probably not an appropriate model for the data.

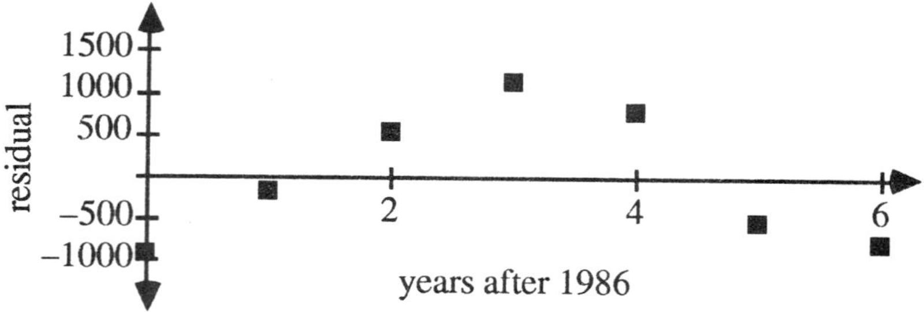

g. Sample response: The average increase in the number of males is less than half as large as the average increase in the number of females. The average increase in total workers is the sum of the averages for males and females. **Note:** Students may also recognize that the regression equation for total workers is the sum of the two regression equations for males and females.

* * * * * * * * * *

Answers to Summary Assessment

1. a. Sample scatterplot:

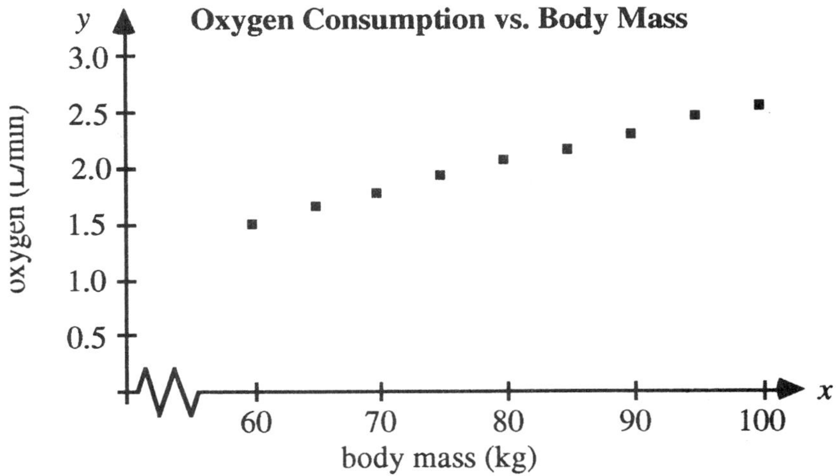

b. 1. The equation of the linear regression is $y = 0.0264x - 0.0642$.

2. The equation of the median-median line is $y = 0.027x - 0.07$.

c. The sum of the squares of the residuals for the median-median line is 0.0042. The sum of the squares of the residuals for the regression line is 0.0019.

d. The following sample graph shows a residual plot for the median-median line.

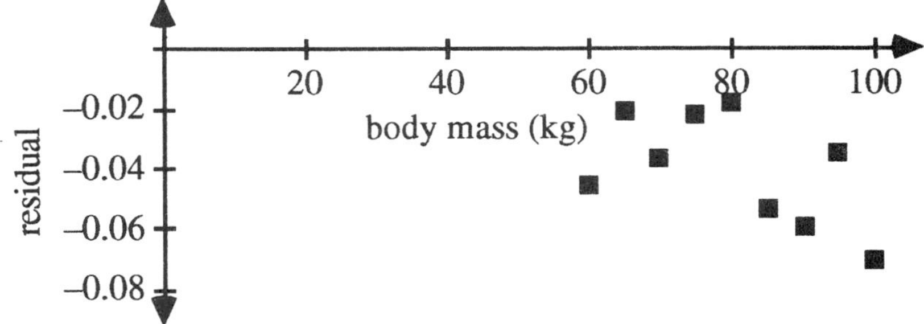

The sample graph below shows a residual plot for the regression line.

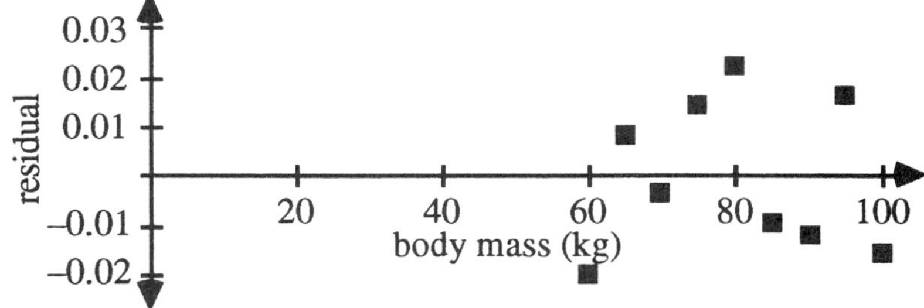

e. Sample response: The equations for the median-median line and the regression line are extremely close. However, the regression line has a smaller sum of the squares of the residuals and a better residual plot. Therefore, the regression line appears to be a better model.

2. Student responses may vary. Some may argue for a linear model since the residuals for the regression line are relatively small. Others may argue against a linear model since the data points appear to follow a power curve and a residual plot reveals a noticeable pattern. In either case, students should support their arguments with graphs, equations, and residuals.

The equation for the regression line is $y = -0.229x + 46.798$. The sum of the squares of the residuals for this model is 35.993.

The equation for the median-median line is $y = -0.245x + 47.682$. The sum of the squares of the residuals for this model is 37.822.

The following graph shows a scatterplot of the data, along with both the regression line and the median-median line:

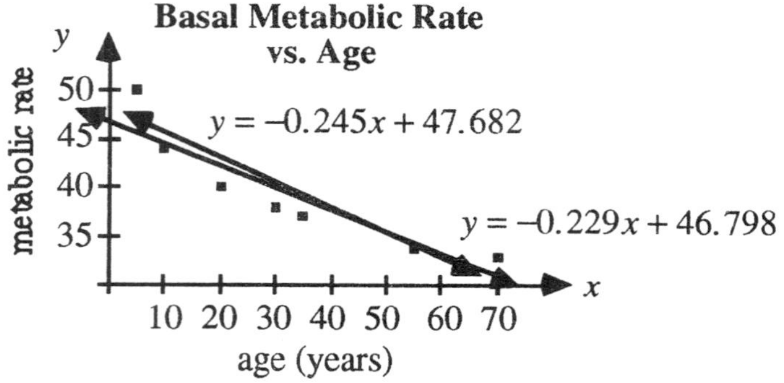

The graph below shows residual plots for these linear models:

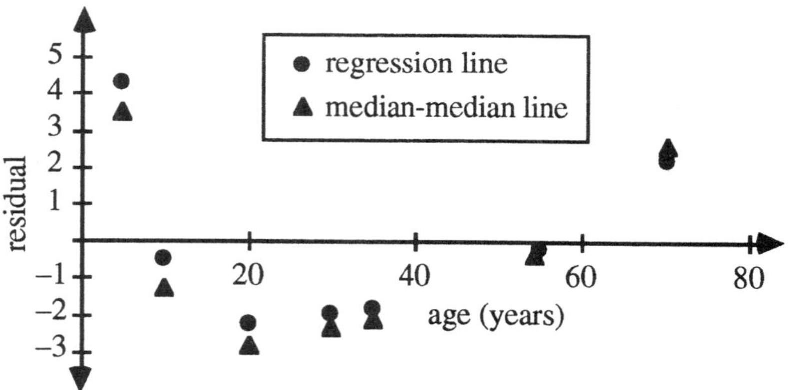

Module Assessment

1. Health professionals often recommend walking as a good way to stay fit. The table below shows some data for the amount of fat expended per minute of walking time.

Minutes of Walking	Fat Expended (kcal/min)
0	0.7
5	1.8
10	1.9
20	2.8
30	3.2
40	3.4
45	3.5

Source: Adapted from Thomas and Londeree, "Calories Expended, Walking vs. Jogging," *The Physician and Sports Medicine* 17 (May 1989): 98.

a. Make a scatterplot of the data.

b. Find the regression line for the data.

c. Find the median-median line for the data.

d. Do the models from Parts **b** and **c** appear to be appropriate for the data? Support your response using graphs, equations, and residuals.

2. The table below shows the domestic motor fuel consumption in the United States for selected years from 1970 to 1991.

Year	Fuel Consumption (in billions of gallons)
1970	92.3
1975	109.0
1980	115.0
1981	114.5
1982	113.4
1983	116.1
1984	118.7
1985	121.3
1986	125.2
1987	127.5
1988	130.1
1989	131.8
1990	130.8
1991	128.6

Source: U.S. Bureau of the Census, 1995.

a. Make a scatterplot of the data.

b. Find the regression line for the data.

c. Find the median-median line for the data.

d. Do the models from Parts **b** and **c** appear to be appropriate for the data? Support your response using graphs, equations, and residuals.

e. 1. Use one of your models to predict the motor fuel consumption in 1993.

   2. According to the Bureau of the Census, the actual motor fuel consumption in 1993 was 137.2 billion gallons. How does your prediction compare with this value?

3. The table below shows the annual milk production in the United States for selected years from 1980 to 1992.

Year	Milk Production (in billions of pounds)
1980	128.4
1985	143.0
1988	145.2
1989	144.2
1990	148.3
1991	148.5
1992	151.8

Source: U.S. Bureau of the Census, 1995.

a. Make a scatterplot of the data.

b. Find the regression line for the data.

c. Find the median-median line for the data.

d. Do the models from Parts **b** and **c** appear to be appropriate for the data? Support your response using graphs, equations, and residuals.

e. 1. Use one of your models to predict the U.S. milk production in 1994.

   2. According to the Bureau of the Census, the actual milk production in 1994 was 153.6 billion pounds. How does your prediction compare with this value?

4. The table below shows the numbers of job-related accidental deaths in the United States for selected years since 1960.

Year	Deaths (in thousands)
1960	13.8
1965	14.1
1970	13.8
1975	13.0
1980	13.2
1984	11.5
1985	11.5
1986	11.1
1987	11.3
1988	11.0
1989	10.9
1990	10.6
1991	9.9

Source: U.S. Bureau of the Census, 1995.

a. Make a scatterplot of the data.

b. Find the regression line for the data.

c. Find the median-median line for the data.

d. Do the models from Parts **b** and **c** appear to be appropriate for the data? Support your response using graphs, equations, and residuals.

e. **1.** Use one of your models to predict the number of job-related deaths in 1993.

2. According to the Bureau of the Census, the actual number of job-related deaths in 1993 was 9100. How does your prediction compare with this value?

5. The cost of health services and supplies has risen dramatically for Americans over the past 30 years. The table below illustrates the increase in total expenditures for medical care since 1970.

Year	Total Expenditures for Health Services and Supplies (in billions of dollars)
1970	69.1
1980	238.9
1984	374.2
1985	407.2
1986	438.9
1987	476.9
1988	526.2
1989	583.2
1990	652.4
1991	728.6

Source: U.S. Bureau of the Census, 1995.

a. Make a scatterplot of the data.

b. Find the regression line for the data.

c. Find the median-median line for the data.

d. Do the models from Parts **b** and **c** appear to be appropriate for the data? Support your response using graphs, equations, and residuals.

Answers to Module Assessment

1. **a.** Sample scatterplot:

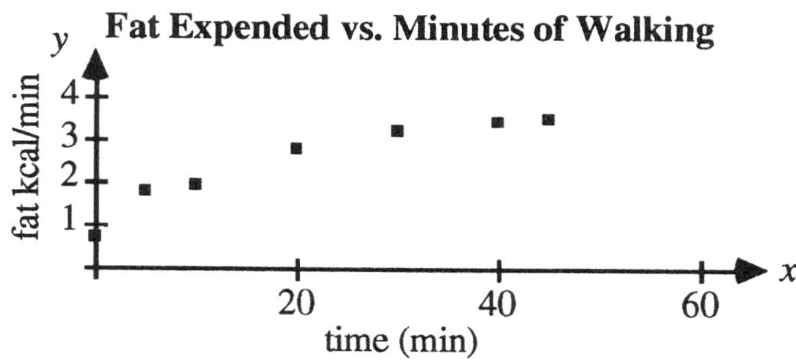

b. The regression line is $y = 0.056x + 1.272$.

c. The median-median line is $y = 0.055x + 1.308$.

d. Both models appear to be reasonable for the data. The sum of the squares of the residuals for the regression line is 0.719, while the sum of the squares of the residuals for the median-median line is 0.722. As shown in the sample graph below, the residual plots also are very similar.

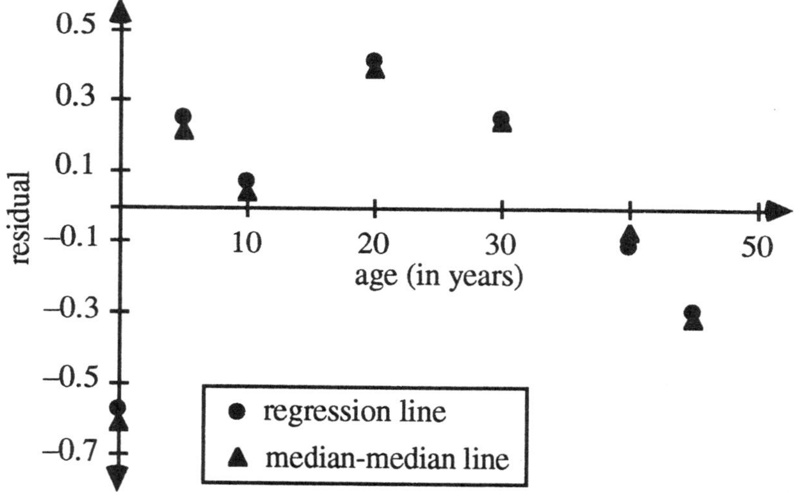

2. **a.** Sample scatterplot:

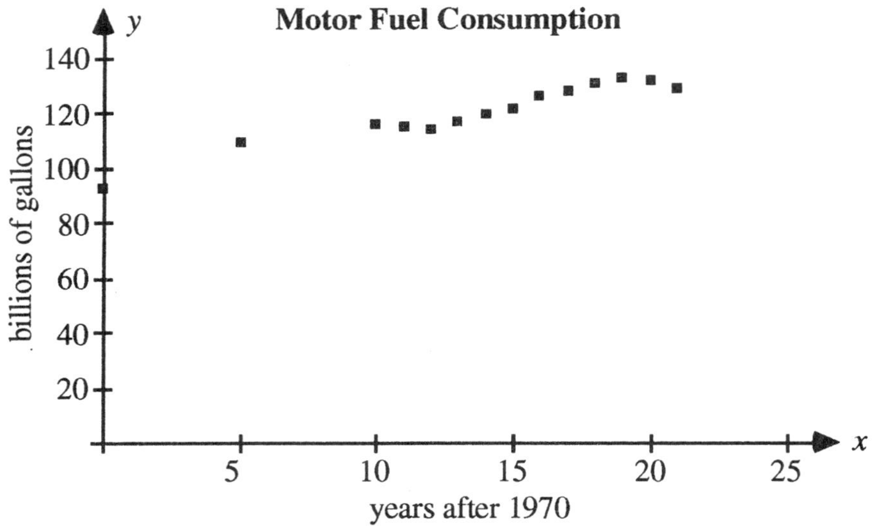

b. Using 1970 as $x = 0$, the regression line is $y = 1.790x + 95.171$.

c. Using 1970 as $x = 0$, the median-median line is $y = 1.856x + 94.261$.

d. Neither line appears to be an appropriate model. The sum of the squares of the residuals for the regression line is 91.88, while the sum of the squares of the residuals for the median-median line is 93.825. As shown in the sample graph below, the residual plots show a definite pattern. (The three "turning points" in the plots indicate that a polynomial of higher degree may be a more appropriate model.)

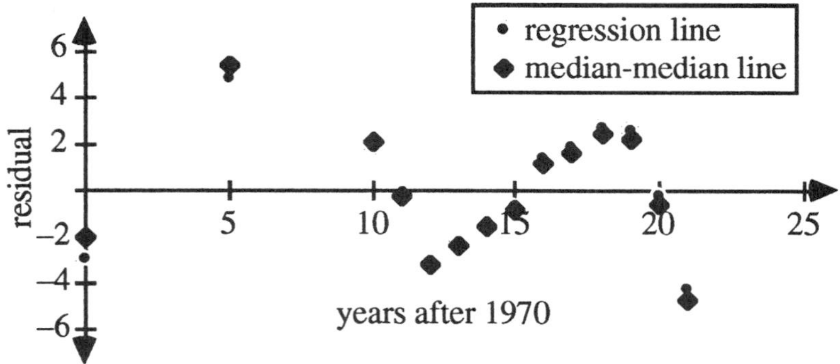

e. **1.** Using the linear regression equation, the predicted fuel consumption is approximately 136.3 billion gallons.

2. The prediction made above is approximately 900 million gallons less than the actual value.

3. **a.** Sample scatterplot:

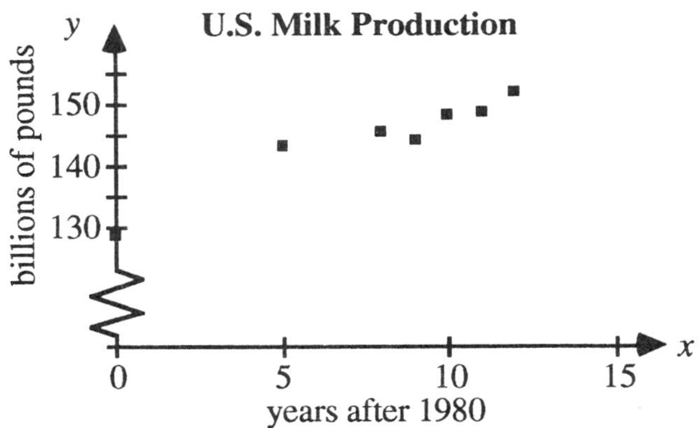

b. Using 1980 as $x = 0$, the regression line is $y = 1.765x + 130.335$.

c. Using 1980 as $x = 0$, the median-median line is $y = 1.606x + 131.374$.

d. Both lines appear to be reasonable models. The sum of the squares of the residuals for the regression line is 24.868, while the sum of the squares of the residuals for the median-median line is 27.756. As shown below, the residual plots are similar.

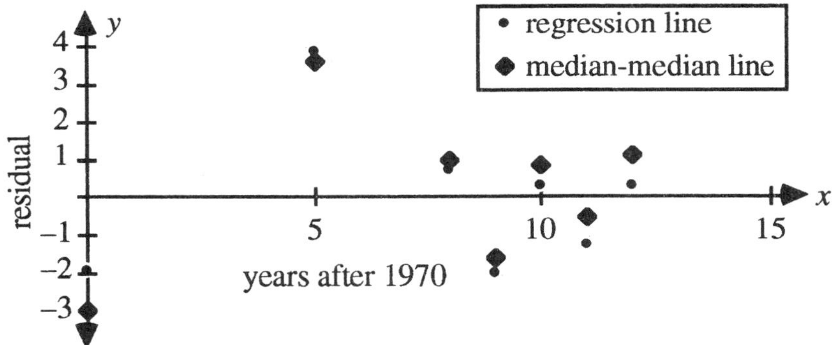

e. **1.** Using the linear regression equation, the predicted milk production is approximately 155 billion pounds.

2. The prediction made above is approximately 1.4 billion pounds more than the actual value.

4. **a.** Sample scatterplot:

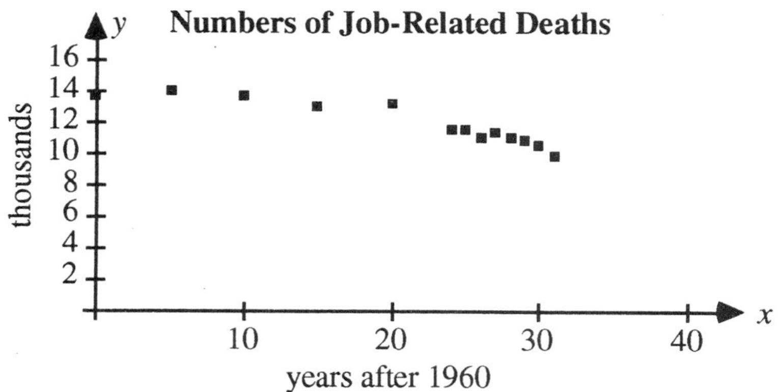

b. Using 1960 as $x = 0$, the regression line is $y = -0.130x + 14.67$.

c. Using 1960 as $x = 0$, the median-median line is $y = -0.139x + 14.882$.

d. Both lines appear to be reasonable models, although some students may observe that the number of deaths seems to be decreasing more rapidly in the 1990s. The sum of the squares of the residuals for the regression line is 8.054, while the sum of the squares of the residuals for the median-median line is 9.328. As shown in the sample graph below, the residual plots are similar.

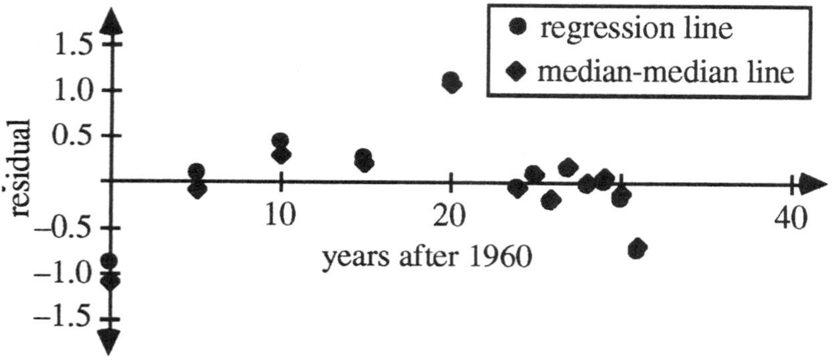

e. **1.** Using the linear regression equation, the predicted number of job-related deaths in 1993 is approximately 10,380.

2. The prediction made above is approximately 1280 more than the actual value.

5. **a.** Sample scatterplot:

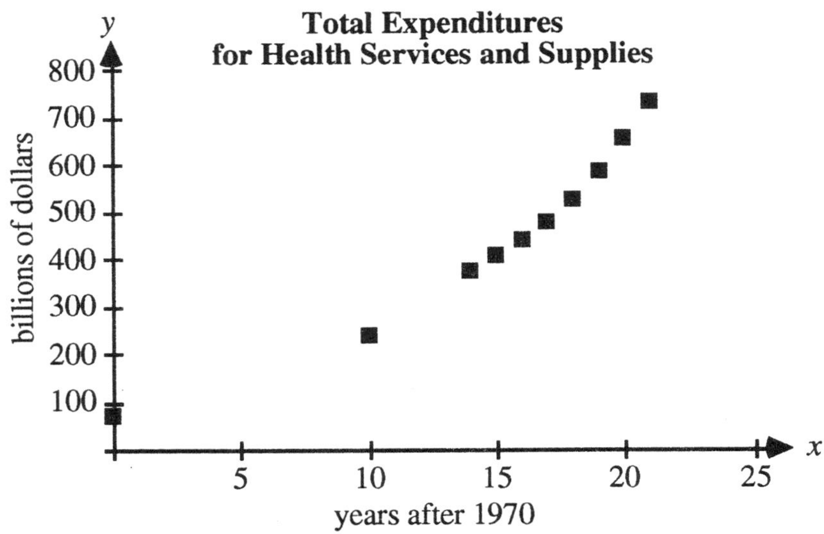

b. Using 1970 as $x = 0$, the regression line is $y = 30.212x - 3.620$.

c. Using 1970 as $x = 0$, the median-median line is $y = 41.350x - 191.192$.

d. Neither line appears to be an appropriate model. The sum of the squares of the residuals for the regression line is 28,037, while the sum of the squares of the residuals for the median-median line is 74,668. The residual plots both show a definite pattern. Students may observe that an exponential equation may be a more appropriate model.

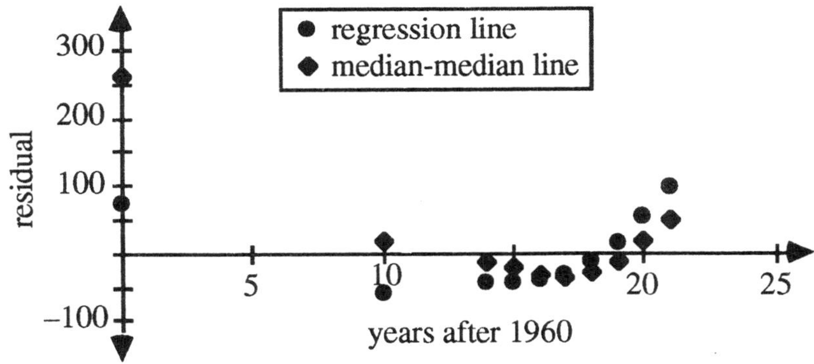

Selected References

McArdle, W. D., F. I. Katch, and V. L. Katch. *Exercise Physiology.* Philadelphia: Lea & Febiger, 1991.

North Carolina School of Science and Mathematics, Department of Mathematics and Computer Science. *Contemporary Precalculus through Applications.* Dedham, MA: Janson Publications, 1992.

Rodahl, K. *The Physiology of Work.* Bristol, PA: Taylor & Francis, 1989.

Thomas, T. R., and B. R. Londeree. "Calories Expended, Walking vs. Jogging." *The Physician and Sports Medicine* 17 (May 1989): 98.

U.S. Bureau of the Census, *Statistical Abstract of the United States: 1995.* Washington, DC: U.S. Government Printing Office, 1995.

Flashbacks

Activity 1

1.1 Determine the equation of the line in the form $y = mx + b$ that contains each of the following pairs of points:

a. A and C

b. B and E

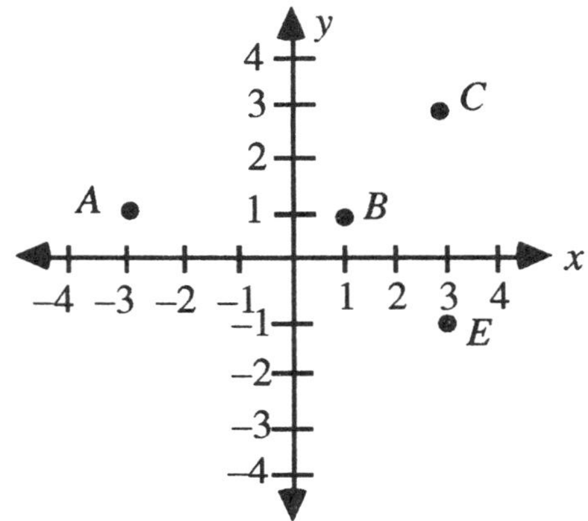

1.2 Given the equation $y = 3x - 2$, determine the value of x for each of the following values of y.

a. $y = 13$

b. $y = -11$

1.3 Given the linear equation $y = -4x + b$, find the value of b when the line contains each of the following points:

a. $(-2,3)$

b. $(1,-2.5)$

Activity 2

2.1 Find the median of the following set of numbers: {12, 45, 32, 81, 65, 24, 35, 26, 48, 50}.

2.2 Determine the equation of the line that passes through the points $(-3,4)$ and $(6,-2)$.

Activity 3

3.1 Determine the slope of the line that passes through each of the following pairs of points:

a. (7,–4) and (2,–5)

b. (1,–2) and (4,–6).

3.2 Find the equation of the line in the form $y = mx + b$ that contains each of the following pairs of points:

a. (1,1) and (5,5)

b. (1,–2) and (4,–6).

Answers to Flashbacks

Activity 1

1.1 **a.** $y = \frac{1}{3}x + 2$

b. $y = -1x + 2$

1.2 **a.** $x = 5$

b. $x = -3$

1.3 **a.** $b = -5$

b. $b = 1.5$

Activity 2

2.1 The median is 40.

2.2 $y = -\frac{2}{3}x + 2$

Activity 3

3.1 **a.** 1/5

b. −4/3

3.2 **a.** $y = x$

b. $y = -\frac{4}{3}x - \frac{2}{3}$

Take It to the Limit

What do hungry chickens, chain letters, and the perimeters of nested triangles have in common? This module introduces you to infinite sequences—and their limits.

Todd Fife • Mark Lutz • Lisa Wood

Teacher Edition

Take It to the Limit

Overview

In this module, students explore arithmetic and geometric sequences and series. They are introduced to limits through infinite geometric sequences and series.

Objectives

In this module, students will:

- identify sequences that are arithmetic, geometric, or neither
- develop formulas for finite arithmetic and geometric series
- develop a formula for certain infinite geometric series
- explore limits graphically and geometrically.

Prerequisites

For this module, students should know:

- how to interpret subscript notation
- how to find explicit and recursive formulas for arithmetic sequences
- how to find explicit and recursive formulas for geometric sequences.

Time Line

Activity	1	2	3	4	Summary Assessment	Total
Days	3	2	2	2	1	10

Materials Required

Materials	Activity				
	1	2	3	4	Summary Assessment
graph paper			X		

Technology

Software	Activity				
	1	**2**	**3**	**4**	**Summary Assessment**
geometry utility				X	X
graphing utility				X	
spreadsheet	X	X	X	X	X
symbolic manipulator	X	X	X	X	X

Take It to the Limit

Introduction

In this introduction, students review arithmetic and geometric sequences along with explicit and recursive formulas.

Discussion

a.

1. This is an arithmetic sequence. The first term is 7 and the common difference is 6. The next term is 31.
2. This is a geometric sequence. The first term is 162 and the common ratio is 1/3. The next term is 2.
3. Sample response: This is a sequence of figures. Each figure is a set of dots forming a right triangle with n dots on each leg and on the hypotenuse, where n is the figure number. The next figure is:

4. This is a geometric sequence. The first term is –7 and the common ratio is –7. The next term is –16,807.
5. This is a sequence of closed intervals. The left-hand value of the interval is always 2, while the right-hand value is $2+(1/n)$, for $n=1,\ 2,\ 3,\ 4,\ \ldots$. The next interval is [2, 2.2].
6. This is a Fibonacci sequence. The first two terms are 4 and 5. Each successive term is the sum of the previous two terms. The next term is 37.

b. A sample formula for each sequence shown below.

1. $\begin{cases} a_1 = 7 \\ a_n = a_{n-1} + 6 \text{ for } n > 1 \end{cases}$
2. $\begin{cases} a_1 = 162 \\ a_n = a_{n-1}(1/3) \text{ for } n > 1 \end{cases}$
3. Although it is not possible to write a recursive formula for the sequence of figures, the number of dots in each figure can be described as follows:

$$\begin{cases} a_1 = 1 \\ a_n = a_{n-1} + n,\ n > 1 \end{cases}$$

4. $\begin{cases} a_1 = -7 \\ a_n = -7a_{n-1} \text{ for } n > 1 \end{cases}$

5. A recursive formula for the right-hand value in each interval is shown below:

$$\begin{cases} a_1 = 3 \\ a_n = a_{n-1} - \dfrac{1}{n(n-1)} \text{ for } n > 1 \end{cases}$$

6. $\begin{cases} a_1 = 4 \\ a_2 = 5 \\ a_n = a_{n-2} + a_{n-1} \text{ for } n > 2 \end{cases}$

c. A sample formula for each sequence shown below.

1. $a_n = 7 + 6(n-1)$ for $n \geq 1$

2. $a_n = 162(1/3)^{n-1}$ for $n \geq 1$

3. Although it is not possible to write an explicit formula for the sequence of figures, the number of dots in each figure can be described as follows:

$$a_n = \frac{n(n+1)}{2}$$

4. $a_n = -7(-7)^{n-1}$ for $n \geq 1$

5. An explicit formula for the right-hand value in each interval is shown below:

$$b_n = 2 + \frac{1}{n}$$

6. Determining an explicit formula for this sequence is beyond the scope of this module.

d. 1. The sequence in Step **1** is arithmetic.

2. The sequences in Steps **2** and **4** are geometric.

e. Sample response: The common difference of an arithmetic sequence can be found by subtracting any term from the following term.

f. Sample response: The common ratio of a geometric sequence can be found by dividing any term by the previous term.

Activity 1

This activity continues the review of arithmetic and geometric sequences, as well as recursive and explicit formulas. **Note:** These concepts were introduced in the Level 1 module "From Rock Bands to Recursion."

Materials List

- none

Technology

- spreadsheet (optional)
- symbolic manipulator (optional)

Exploration

This exploration is designed for groups of four students. To ensure equal participation, each student should create a sequence, and each group should pass in a consistent clockwise or counterclockwise rotation.

The following responses describe a sample game.

a. The first student creates an arithmetic sequence with a common difference of –2 and a first term of 20. The student writes down the first five terms—20, 18, 16, 14, 12—and passes the sheet of paper to the second student.

b. The second student identifies the sequence as arithmetic and writes this below the first five terms. The student then writes the following rule: "To make this sequence, start with 20 and add –2 (or subtract 2) every time to get the next term."

c. The third student uses this algorithm to write the recursive formula

$$\begin{cases} a_1 = 20 \\ a_n = a_{n-1} + (-2) \text{ for } n > 1 \end{cases}$$

and the explicit formula $a_n = 20 + (-2)(n-1)$ for $n \geq 1$.

d. The fourth student uses these formulas to write the first five terms of the sequence: 20, 18, 16, 14, 12.

e. The first student compares the sequence written by the fourth student with the original sequence. (If the terms do not match, the group should examine the paper and identify the source of the mistake.)

Discussion

a. Responses will vary.

b. Sample response: For arithmetic sequences, the difference between consecutive terms must be the same. For geometric sequences, the ratio of any two successive terms must be the same. A sequence that does not have a common ratio or a common difference between successive terms is neither arithmetic nor geometric.

c.
1. If the sequence is arithmetic with a common difference of 1, the next three terms will be 4, 5, 6.

2. If the next term in the sequence is the sum of the two previous terms, then the next three terms will be 5, 8, 13.

3. If the next term in the sequence is the sum of the previous three terms, then the next three terms will be 6, 11, 20.

d. Sample response: No. Since the sequence is defined as arithmetic, then there must be a common difference. Therefore, the next three terms cannot vary.

Assignment

1.1
a. The first five terms are 9, 6, 3, 0, –3.

b. The first five terms are –5, –6.5, –8.45, –10.985, –14.2805.

1.2
a. $99 = 11 + 2(n-1) \Rightarrow n = 45$

b. $6.5536 = 20(0.8)^{n-1} \Rightarrow n = 6$

c. $357 = 7 + 3.5(n-1) \Rightarrow n = 101$

d. $3072 = 3(2)^{n-1} \Rightarrow n = 11$

***1.3**
a. **1.** Two possible terms are 63, 127.

2. The explicit formula is $a_n = 2^n - 1$ for $n \geq 1$. The recursive formula is:

$$\begin{cases} a_1 = 1 \\ a_n = a_{n-1} + 2^{n-1} \text{ for } n > 1 \end{cases}$$

3. The sequence is neither arithmetic nor geometric.

b. **1.** Two possible terms are –2/25, 2/125.

2. The explicit formula is $g_n = -50(-1/5)^{n-1}$ for $n \geq 1$. The recursive formula is:

$$\begin{cases} g_1 = -50 \\ g_n = (-1/5)g_{n-1} \text{ for } n > 1 \end{cases}$$

3. The sequence is geometric.

c. 1. Two possible terms are 13, 16.

2. The explicit formula is $a_n = 1 + 3(n-1)$ for $n \geq 1$. The recursive formula is:

$$\begin{cases} a_1 = 1 \\ a_n = a_{n-1} + 3 \text{ for } n > 1 \end{cases}$$

3. This is an arithmetic sequence.

d. 1. Two possible terms are $2\frac{1}{6}$, $2\frac{1}{7}$.

2. The explicit formula is:

$$a_n = 2 + \frac{1}{n+1} \text{ for } n \geq 1$$

The recursive formula is:

$$\begin{cases} a_1 = 2\frac{1}{2} \\ a_n = a_{n-1} - \dfrac{1}{n(n+1)} \text{ for } n > 1 \end{cases}$$

3. This sequence is neither arithmetic nor geometric.

e. 1. Two possible terms are 6, –6.

2. The explicit formula is $a_n = 6(-1)^{n-1}$ for $n \geq 1$. The recursive formula is:

$$\begin{cases} a_1 = 6 \\ a_n = -1(a_{n-1}) \text{ for } n > 1 \end{cases}$$

3. This sequence is geometric.

1.4 **a.** Any geometric sequence with a common ratio of 1 is also an arithmetic sequence with a common difference of 0. For example, the following sequence is both arithmetic and geometric:

$$\pi, \pi, \pi, \pi, \pi, \ldots$$

b. An explicit formula for the sample sequence given in Part **a** is $a_n = \pi + 0(n-1)$ for $n \geq 1$.

c. An explicit formula for the sample sequence given in Part **a** is $g_n = \pi \bullet (1)^{n-1}$ for $n \geq 1$.

1.5 **a.** The common difference can be found by solving the following equation:

$$93 = 13 + d(50 - 1)$$
$$d = 80/49$$

b. The common ratio can be found by solving the equation below:

$$192 = 12 \bullet r^{5-1}$$
$$r = \pm 2$$

c. The common difference is 3 and the number of terms is 18.

d. The common ratio is 5 and the number of terms is 10.

1.6 Sample response: The dog's mass would be 43.2 kg. If the dog's loss of mass is actually an arithmetic sequence, then the dog would lose 0.9 kg per month for 12 months—a total of 10.8 kg. Depending on the size of the animal, this might not be reasonable. The veterinarian would not let the dog's mass fall below a healthy level.

1.7 **a.** Sample response: If the mass of a chick is 36 g when hatched, and it gains 10% of its mass each day for 8 weeks, then its daily mass is a geometric sequence with the following formula: $g_n = 36 \bullet 1.1^{n-1}$. After 56 days, the chick's mass would be about 6.8 kg.

b. This is probably not reasonable. Students may know from experience that the mass of a broiler chicken is typically under 2 kg. According to most poultry growers, the mass of an 8-week-old chicken should be about 43 times its mass at birth, or about 1548 g.

c. The advertiser should claim a 7% daily mass gain.

1.8 The following sample responses assume that the first term is positive.

a. If the common ratio is between –1 and 0, then the sequence will alternate between positive and negative terms and will get progressively closer to 0.

b. If the common ratio is between 0 and 1, then the sequence will get progressively closer to 0.

c. If the common ratio is less than –1, then the sequence will alternate between positive and negative terms. The absolute value of the terms will get progressively larger.

d. If the common ratio is greater than 1, the terms of the sequence will get progressively larger.

* * * * *

***1.9** **a–b.** Students generate sequences by paper folding.

c. The explicit formula for the area of the top surface (in cm^2) is $g_n = 128 \bullet (0.5)^{n-1}$ for $n \geq 1$. The recursive formula for the area of the top surface is:

$$\begin{cases} g_1 = 128 \\ g_n = g_{n-1} \bullet 0.5 \text{ for } n > 1 \end{cases}$$

d. The explicit formula for the number of layers is $g_n = 2 \bullet 2^{n-1}$ for $n \geq 1$. The recursive formula for the number of layers is:

$$\begin{cases} g_1 = 2 \\ g_n = g_{n-1} \bullet 2 \text{ for } n > 1 \end{cases}$$

e. As the number of folds increases, the area of the top surface appears to approach 0 cm^2.

f. As the number of folds increases, the number of layers becomes larger and larger.

1.10 **a.** The sheet of paper would have to have an area of about $5.6 \bullet 10^{14}$ cm^2. Its dimensions would be about $2.4 \bullet 10^7$ cm (or 240 km) on each side.

b. Answers will vary, depending on the thickness of the paper. If a single layer were 0.1 mm thick, the height of the stack after 50 cuts would be about $1.1 \bullet 10^8$ km.

1.11 **a.** This is a Fibonacci sequence with the first two terms equal to 1. It is neither arithmetic nor geometric.

b. This is a geometric sequence with a common ratio of 1.05 and a first term of 2.

c. This is an arithmetic sequence with a common difference of –1000 and a first term of 2000.

d. This sequence (0, 1, 3, 6, 10, 15, 21, ...) is neither arithmetic nor geometric. The pattern can be described by the recursive formula.

e. This sequence is neither arithmetic nor geometric. The first term is 3/1. In each successive term, the numerator remains constant at 3 and the denominator increases by 1.

1.12 **a.** The terms increase without bound.

b. The terms increase without bound.

c. The terms decrease without bound.

d. The terms increase without bound.

e. The terms approach 0.

* * * * * * * * * *

Activity 2

This activity introduces students to finite arithmetic series and their expanded form.

Materials List

- none

Technology

- spreadsheet (optional)
- symbolic manipulator (optional)

Exploration

a. **1.** Sample response:

$$\begin{array}{rcrcrcccrcr} S_{1000} & = & 1 & + & 2 & + & \cdots & + & 999 & + & 1000 \\ S_{1000} & = & 1000 & + & 999 & + & \cdots & + & 2 & + & 1 \\ \hline 2S_{1000} & = & 1001 & + & 1001 & + & \cdots & + & 1001 & + & 1001 \end{array}$$

Since there are a total of 1000 terms of 1001:

$$S_{1000} = \frac{1000 \bullet 1001}{2} = 500{,}500$$

2. Sample response:

$$\begin{array}{rcrcrcccrcr} S_n & = & n & + & (n-1) & + & \cdots & + & 2 & + & 1 \\ S_n & = & 1 & + & 2 & + & \cdots & + & (n-1) & + & n \\ \hline 2S_n & = & (n+1) & + & (n+1) & + & \cdots & + & (n+1) & + & (n+1) \end{array}$$

Since there are a total of n terms of $(n+1)$:

$$S_n = \frac{n \bullet (n+1)}{2}$$

b. Sample response:

$$\begin{array}{rcrcrcccrcr} S_{50} & = & 2 & + & 4 & + & \cdots & + & 998 & + & 100 \\ S_{50} & = & 100 & + & 998 & + & \cdots & + & 4 & + & 2 \\ \hline 2S_{50} & = & 102 & + & 102 & + & \cdots & + & 102 & + & 102 \end{array}$$

Since there are a total of 50 terms of 102:

$$S_{50} = \frac{50 \bullet (102)}{2} = 2550$$

c. Using the explicit formula for an arithmetic sequence, $a_{75} = 2 + (75 - 1) \bullet 4 = 298$. Given this value, students should use a method like the one employed in Parts **a** and **b**:

$$\begin{array}{rcccccccccc} S_{75} & = & 2 & + & 6 & + & \cdots & + & 294 & + & 298 \\ S_{75} & = & 298 & + & 294 & + & \cdots & + & 6 & + & 2 \\ \hline 2S_{75} & = & 300 & + & 300 & + & \cdots & + & 300 & + & 300 \end{array}$$

Since there are a total of 75 terms of 300:

$$S_{75} = \frac{75 \bullet (300)}{2} = 11{,}250$$

d. **1.** $a_2 = a_1 + d,\ a_3 = a_1 + 2d,\ a_4 = a_1 + 3d$

2. $a_n = a_1 + (n-1) \bullet d,\ a_{n-1} = a_1 + (n-2) \bullet d,\ a_{n-2} = a_1 + (n-3) \bullet d,$ $a_{n-3} = a_1 + (n-4) \bullet d$

3. Using a method like the one employed in Parts **a** and **b**:

$$\begin{array}{rcccccc} S_n & = & a_1 + & [a_1 + d] + & \cdots + & [a_1 + (n-2)d] + & [a_1 + (n-1)d] \\ S_n & = & [a_1 + (n-1)d] + & [a_1 + (n-2)d] + & \cdots + & [a_1 + d] + & a_1 \\ \hline 2S_n & = & [2a_1 + (n-1)d] + & [2a_1 + (n-1)d] + & \cdots + & [2a_1 + (n-1)d] + & [2a_1 + (n-1)d] \end{array}$$

Since there are a total of *n* terms of $[2a_1 + (n-1)d]$:

$$S_n = \frac{n \bullet [2a_1 + (n-1)d]}{2} = na_1 + \frac{n \bullet [(n-1)d]}{2}$$

Discussion

a. The equation below

$$S_n = \frac{n}{2}[2a_1 + (n-1) \bullet d]$$

can be expanded as follows:

$$S_n = \frac{n}{2}[a_1 + a_1 + (n-1) \bullet d]$$

Since $a_n = a_1 + (n-1) \bullet d$, students can make the following substitution:

$$Sn = \frac{n}{2}(a_1 + a_n)$$

b. The sequences in Parts **a** and **b** are arithmetic sequences because there is a common difference between consecutive terms.

c. **1.** Sample response: The sum of the first 100 even numbers should be twice the sum of the first 100 natural numbers because:

$$2+4+6+\cdots+200=2(1+2+3+\cdots+100)=2(5050)=10{,}100$$

2. The sum of the first 100 multiples of k can be found as follows:

$$\begin{aligned} k+2k+3k+\cdots+99k+100k &= k(1+2+3+\cdots+99+100) \\ &= k\frac{100(101)}{2}=5050k \end{aligned}$$

d. Sample response: If the common difference is positive, the sum of the infinite arithmetic series will increase without bound. If the common difference is negative, the sum of the infinite arithmetic series will decrease without bound.

Assignment

2.1 The sum of the first n even numbers can be found as follows:

$$\begin{aligned} S_n &= \frac{n}{2}(2+2n) \\ &= \frac{n}{2}\bullet 2(1+n) \\ &= n(n+1) \end{aligned}$$

2.2 Student methods may vary. Using the formula from Part **a** of the exploration:

$$S_n=\frac{n(n+1)}{2}=\frac{2000(2000+1)}{2}=2{,}001{,}000$$

2.3 **a.** Sample response:

$$\begin{aligned} k+2k+3k+\cdots+(n-1)k+nk &= k(1+2+3+\cdots+(n-1)+n) \\ &= k\frac{n(n+1)}{2} \end{aligned}$$

b. The sum can be found as follows:

$$\frac{3(600)(600+1)}{2}=540{,}900$$

***2.4** **a.** The first term of the sequence is 3.

b. The common difference is 4.

c. Using the explicit formula for an arithmetic sequence:

$$\begin{aligned} 451 &= 3+4(n-1) \\ 113 &= n \end{aligned}$$

d. The sum is the finite arithmetic series $3 + 7 + 11 + \cdots + 451$. Using the formula for an arithmetic series:

$$S_{113} = \frac{113}{2}(3 + 451) = 25{,}561$$

2.5 Sample response: No, because the sum of each pair of numbers is not constant. For example, given the sequence 32, 16, 8, 4, 2, 1, the sums of the pairs are 33, 18, 12, 18, and 33.

***2.6** **a.** Sample response: The monthly payments may be considered an arithmetic sequence where the first term is $106.26 and the common difference is 0.

b. Sample response: Yes. Since the payments themselves form an arithmetic sequence, their indicated sum forms an arithmetic series.

c. The lessee pays $150.00 + $1,600.00 + (36 • $106.26) or $5575.36, of which $150.00 is refunded at the end of the lease.

d. Sample response: The difference of $3312.64 may be the cost to purchase the car at the end of the lease. Or it may be that the car costs an additional $8,888.00 at the end of the lease.

* * * * *

2.7 The number of newspapers delivered each week forms an arithmetic sequence where $a_1 = 15{,}000$ and $d = 50$. Using the formula for an arithmetic series:

$$S_{52} = \frac{52}{2}(2 \bullet 15{,}000 + 51 \bullet 50) = 846{,}300$$

2.8 **a.** The first three terms are –2, 3, 8.

b. $a_{150} = -7 + 5 \bullet 150 = 743$

c. $S_{150} = \frac{150}{2}(-2 + 743) = 55{,}575$

2.9 **a.** $S_{41} = \frac{41}{2}(5 + 120) = 2562.5$

b. $d = \frac{(120 - 5)}{(41 - 1)} = 2.875$

c. The second and third terms of the sequence are 7.875 and 10.75.

* * * * * * * * * *

Activity 3

In this activity, students develop an algorithm for finding the sum of the terms of a finite geometric sequence.

Materials List

- graph paper (two sheets per student)

Technology

- spreadsheet
- symbolic manipulator (optional)

Exploration

a. The number of e-mail addresses received is 6.

b. Since 6 people send 3 letters each, the second group consists of $6 \bullet 3 = 18$ people. If all decide to participate, the number of e-mail addresses received is 18.

c. The number of e-mail addresses received at the third stage is 54, at the fourth stage is 162, and at the fifth stage is 486.

d. The number of e-mail addresses received at each stage forms the following geometric sequence: 6, 18, 54, ..., $6 \bullet 3^{199}$.

e. The following geometric series (equation 1) represents the total number of addresses received:

$$S_{200} = 6 + 18 + 54 + \cdots + 6 \bullet 3^{197} + 6 \bullet 3^{198} + 6 \bullet 3^{199}$$

f.

1. Multiplying both sides of the equation above by 3 yields equation 2:

$$3S_{200} = 18 + 54 + 162 + \cdots + 6 \bullet 3^{198} + 6 \bullet 3^{199} + 6 \bullet 3^{200}$$

2. Subtracting equation 1 from equation 2 as shown below:

$$\begin{array}{l} 3S_{200} = 18 + 54 + \cdots + 6 \bullet 3^{197} + 6 \bullet 3^{198} + 6 \bullet 3^{199} + 6 \bullet 3^{200} \\ \underline{-(S_{200} = 6 + 18 + 54 + \cdots + 6 \bullet 3^{197} + 6 \bullet 3^{198} + 6 \bullet 3^{199})} \\ 2S_{200} = 6 \bullet 3^{200} - 6 \end{array}$$

3. Solving for S_{200}, the number of e-mail addresses is:

$$S_{200} = \frac{6 \bullet 3^{200} - 6}{2} \approx 7.96842 \bullet 10^{95}$$

g. Student answers may vary, but the general formula should appear as follows:

$$S = \frac{g_1 r^n - g_1}{r-1} = \frac{g_1(r^n - 1)}{r-1}$$

Discussion

a. Sample response: If the chain is unbroken, we would expect to receive approximately $7.96842 \bullet 10^{95}$ e-mail addresses. This is not reasonable, since it far exceeds the earth's population.

b. Sample response: Chain letters on e-mail are probably illegal because of the ease with which someone could send thousands of letters at once. This creates too much potential for fraud and abuse.

c. Answers may vary, but the general formula should appear as follows:

$$S = \frac{g_1 r^n - g_1}{r-1} = \frac{g_1(r^n - 1)}{r-1}$$

Note: Some students may have obtained the equivalent form shown below (found by multiplying both the numerator and the denominator by –1):

$$S = \frac{g_1(1 - r^n)}{1-r}$$

d. Sample response: If r equals 1, the denominator in the formula is 0. This makes the value of the fraction undefined.

e.

1. Sample response: 4, 4, 4, ...

2. Sample response: If r is 1, then each term is equal to the first term, and the sequence is arithmetic with a common difference of 0. The sum of n terms can be found as follows: $S_n = n \bullet g_1$.

f.

1. These are equivalent by using the distributive property and factoring out g_1.

2. These are equivalent by factoring out r from $g_1 r^n$ and substituting g_n for $g_1 r^{n-1}$.

g. Sample response: Find the common ratio, then use the formula below:

$$S_n = \frac{g_n r - g_1}{r-1}$$

Note: In the assignment, students should be encouraged to use the formula that is most appropriate for the given information.

Assignment

3.1 **a.** $S_{17} = \frac{(3.5)(0.6)^{17} - 3.5}{0.6 - 1} \approx 8.75$

b. $S_{10} = \frac{(10)(10)^{10} - 10}{10 - 1} = 11{,}111{,}111{,}110$

3.2 **a.** $S = \frac{(6.5536)(0.8) - 20}{0.8 - 1} \approx 73.79$

b. $S = \frac{(3072)2 - 3}{2 - 1} = 6141$

3.3 **a.** This is an arithmetic series.

$$S_{45} = \frac{45}{2}(11 + 99) = 2475$$

b. This is an arithmetic series.

$$S_7 = \frac{7}{2}(2 + (-28)) = -91$$

c. This series is neither arithmetic nor geometric.

$$S_6 = \frac{1903}{140} \approx 13.59$$

d. This is a geometric series.

$$S_5 = \frac{\frac{1}{2} \bullet \left(\frac{1}{2}\right)^5 - \frac{1}{2}}{\frac{1}{2} - 1} = \frac{31}{32} \approx 0.97$$

***3.4** **a.** Sample response: When the tortoise has run 1.11111 m, six time intervals have elapsed.

b. To determine the total distance Achilles covered, I could multiply the distance covered by the tortoise by 10, or use the formula for a finite geometric series:

$$S_6 = \left(\frac{10(0.1)^6 - 10}{0.1 - 1}\right) = 11.1111$$

c. Sample response: No, with its 10-m head start, the tortoise is 11.11111 m from Achilles' starting point. After six time intervals, Achilles has only traveled 11.1111 m. He is still 0.00001 m behind.

d. Students may respond in a number of different ways. Some possible responses are given below:

- No, because the tortoise would always be some distance ahead of Achilles, even though that distance is getting smaller and smaller.
- Yes, because the lead of the tortoise will become so small that it will be impossible to determine if the tortoise is ahead.
- Yes, because if Achilles travels 10 m/sec, in 2 sec, he will cover 20 m while the tortoise—who travels 1/10 as fast, or 1 m/sec—will have moved only 12 m (including the 10-m head start). Therefore, at some time during the first 2 sec, Achilles must pass the tortoise.
- Yes, because the total distance traveled by both Achilles and the tortoise appears to approach a maximum of $11\frac{1}{9}$ m.

***3.5** **a.** Using the formula for the sum of a geometric series, the total number of wheat kernels in the reward is:

$$S_{64} = \frac{1 \bullet 2^{64} - 1}{2 - 1} \approx 1.8 \bullet 10^{19}$$

b. The wheat would cover approximately $2.4 \bullet 10^7$ km^2.

c. The wheat would be 24 layers thick

3.6 Using the formula for the sum of a geometric series, the total number of wheat kernels in the reward is:

$$S_{64} = \left(\frac{1(3)^{64} - 1}{3 - 1} \right) \approx 1.72 \bullet 10^{30}$$

This is enough wheat to cover the United States with approximately 2.3 trillion layers. **Note:** This is a good opportunity to compare the magnitudes of numbers like 2^{64} and 3^{64}.

***3.7** **a.** The first six terms of the sequence are illustrated below:

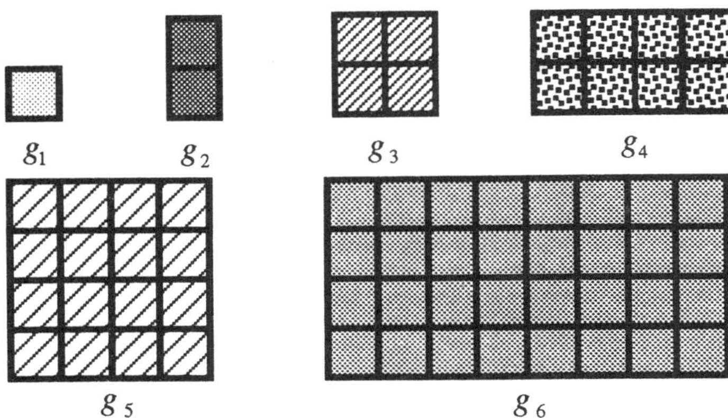

b. **1.** Sample response:

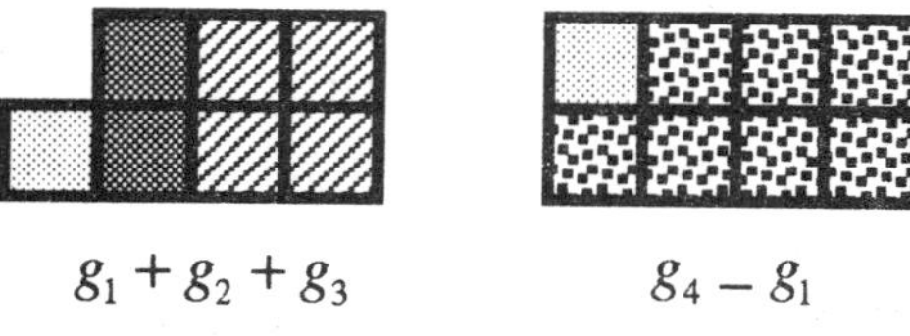

$g_1 + g_2 + g_3$ $\quad$ $g_4 - g_1$

=

2. Sample response:

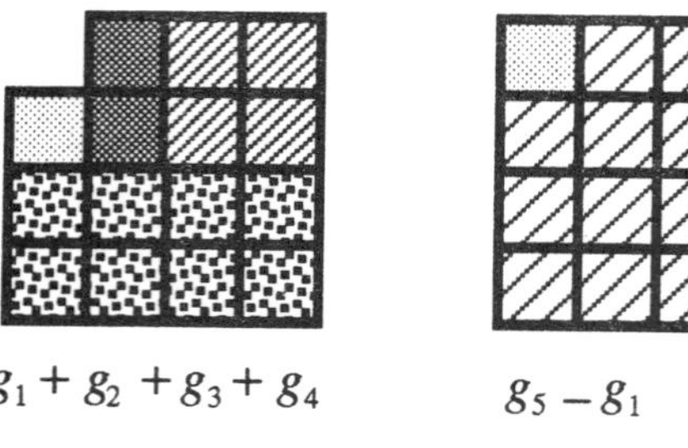

$g_1 + g_2 + g_3 + g_4$ $\quad$ $g_5 - g_1$

=

3. Sample response:

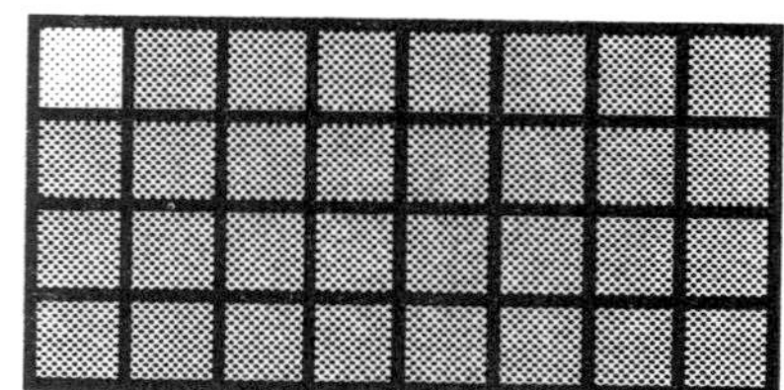

$g_1 + g_2 + g_3 + g_4 + g_5$ $\quad$ $g_6 - g_1$

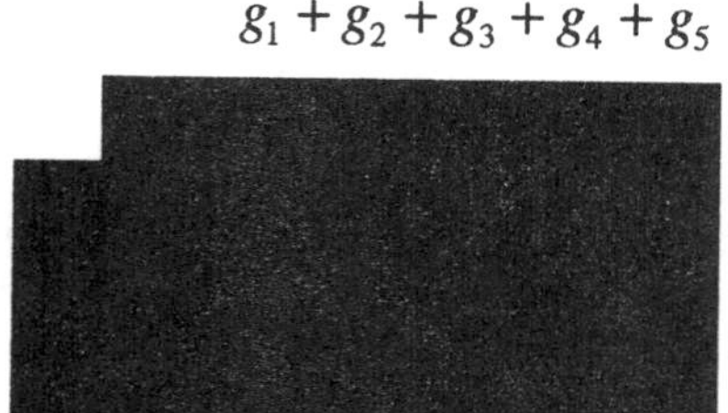

=

c. Sample response: The sum of the terms is equal to the difference between the term following the last term of the series and the first term of the series, or $g_1 + g_2 + g_3 + \cdots + g_n = g_{n+1} - g_1$.

d. Sample response: The sum of a geometric series can be found using the formula:

$$S_n = \frac{g_n r - g_1}{r - 1}$$

In this series *r* is 2. By substituting 2 for *r*, the formula becomes:

$$S_n = \frac{g_n(2) - g_1}{2 - 1}$$

or $S_n = g_n(2) - g_1$. Since $g_n r$ represents the term following g_n, g_{n+1} can be substituted for $g_n(2)$. The result is $S_n = g_{n+1} - g_1$.

* * * * *

3.8 **a.** The geometric sequence is: 6, 4.8, 3.84, …, $6(0.8)^{n-1}$.

b. $S_n = 6 + 4.8 + 3.84 + \cdots + 6(0.8)^{n-1}$

c. **1.** $S_{10} = \dfrac{6(0.8)^{10} - 6}{0.8 - 1} \approx 26.78$ m

2. $S_{20} = \dfrac{6(0.8)^{20} - 6}{0.8 - 1} \approx 29.65$ m

3. $S_{30} = \dfrac{6(0.8)^{30} - 6}{0.8 - 1} \approx 29.96$ m

4. $S_{40} = \dfrac{6(0.8)^{40} - 6}{0.8 - 1} \approx 30.00$ m

d. **1.** The geometric series appears to approach 30 m.

2. Sample response: The number is the sum of all the heights that the ball reaches.

3.8 **a.** $S_5 = 9 + 6 + 4 + \frac{8}{3} + \frac{16}{9}$ or $S_5 = 9 + 9\left(\frac{2}{3}\right)^1 + 9\left(\frac{2}{3}\right)^2 + 9\left(\frac{2}{3}\right)^3 + 9\left(\frac{2}{3}\right)^4$

b. The common ratio is 2/3.

c. **1.** The height of the tree is:

$$4 + S_{10} = 4 + \frac{9\left(\frac{2}{3}\right)^{10} - 9}{\frac{2}{3} - 1} \approx 30.53 \text{ m}$$

2. The height of the tree is:

$$4+S_{20}=4+\frac{9\left(\frac{2}{3}\right)^{20}-9}{\frac{2}{3}-1}\approx 30.99 \text{ m}$$

3. The height of the tree is:

$$4+S_{30}=4+\frac{9\left(\frac{2}{3}\right)^{30}-9}{\frac{2}{3}-1}\approx 31.00 \text{ m}$$

d. The height appears to approach 31 m.

* * * * * * * * * *

Activity 4

In this activity, students are introduced to limits, sequences that approach limits, and sequences that do not approach limits.

Materials Required

- none

Technology

- graphing utility
- spreadsheet
- geometry utility
- symbolic manipulator (optional)

Exploration

a. Students create a sequence by connecting the midpoints of sides of successive triangles. See Figure **2** in student edition.

b. Sample table:

Term No.	Name of Triangle	Area (cm^2)	Perimeter (cm)	Area of Δ / Area of Previous Δ	Perimeter of Δ / Perimeter of Previous Δ
1	Δ*ABC*	100.2	45.7	none	none
2	Δ*DEF*	25.05	22.9	0.25	0.5
3	Δ*GHJ*	6.3	11.4	0.25	0.5
4	Δ*KLM*	1.6	5.7	0.25	0.5
5	⋮	0.4	2.9	0.25	0.5
6		9.8E–2	1.4	0.25	0.5
7		2.4E–2	7.1E–1	0.25	0.5
8		6.1E–3	3.6E–1	0.25	0.5
9		1.5E–3	1.8E–1	0.25	0.5
10		3.8E–4	8.9E–2	0.25	0.5
11		9.6E–5	4.5E–2	0.25	0.5
12		2.4E–5	2.2E–2	0.25	0.5
13		6.0E–6	1.1E–2	0.25	0.5
14		1.5E–6	5.6E–3	0.25	0.5
15		3.7E–7	2.8E–3	0.25	0.5

c. **1.** See table given in Part **b**.

2. Sample scatterplot:

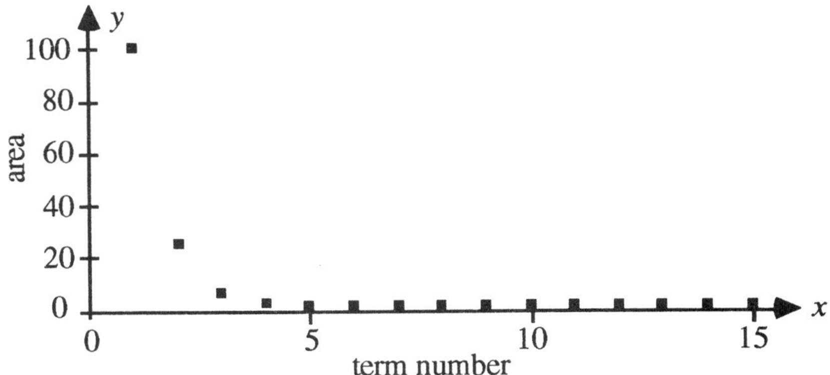

d. 1. See table given in Part **b**.

2. Sample scatterplot:

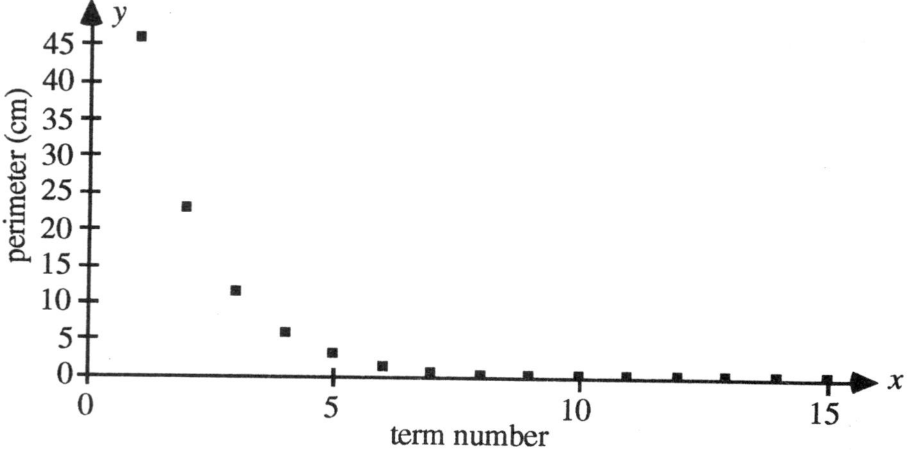

e. **1.** The following table shows the sums for the sample triangle used in Parts **a** and **b** (rounded to the nearest hundredth).

Sum	Area (cm^2)
S_1	100.20
S_2	125.25
S_3	131.51
S_4	133.07
S_5	133.47
S_6	133.57
S_7	133.59
S_8	133.60
S_9	133.60
S_{10}	133.60

2. Sample graph:

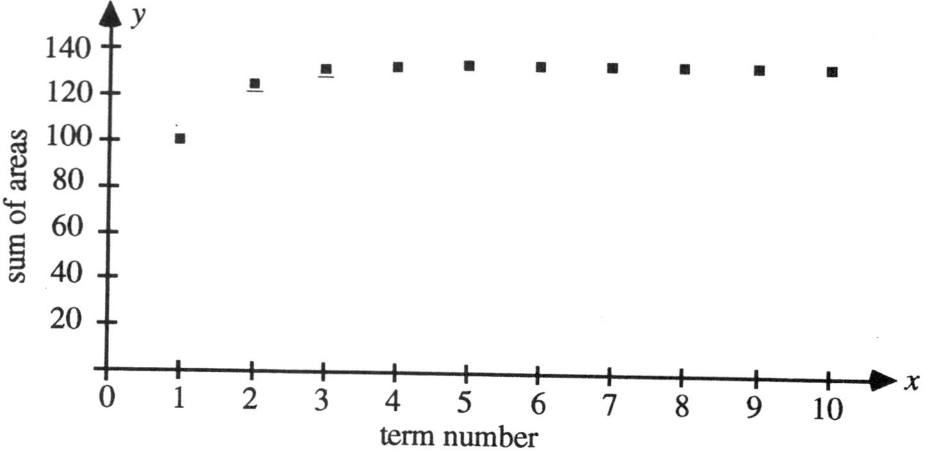

f. The following table shows the sums for the sample triangle used in Parts **a** and **b** (rounded to the nearest hundredth).

Sum	Area (cm^2)
S_{20}	133.60
S_{30}	133.60
S_{50}	133.60
S_{100}	133.60

Discussion

a.
1. The area of each triangle is 1/4 the area of the previous triangle.
2. The perimeter of each triangle is 1/2 the perimeter of the previous triangle.

b.
1. Sample response: The area would approach 0 but never actually reach it.
2. Sample response: The perimeter would approach 0 but never actually reach it.

c. Sample response: When finding a limit, you can choose a prescribed accuracy however small you wish. This prescribed accuracy sets up boundaries above and below the conjectured limit. If all the terms after a certain term lie within the boundaries we picked, no matter how small, we know what the limit is as the number of terms increases indefinitely.

d. Sample response: My answers are consistent with the graphs. The perimeters and areas appear to approach 0 after only a few terms.

e.
1. Sample response: From the spreadsheet, the perimeter of each triangle after the 13th one is within 1/100 of 0.
2. Sample response: From the spreadsheet, the area of each triangle after the 7th one is within 1/100 of 0.

f.
1. As n increases indefinitely, the value of $(1/2)^n$ approaches 0.
2. As n increases indefinitely, the formula approaches the following expression:

$$S = \frac{g_1 \bullet (0-1)}{\frac{1}{2}-1} = \frac{g_1 \bullet -1}{-\frac{1}{2}} = \frac{g_1}{\frac{1}{2}} = 2g_1$$

g.

1. As n increases without bound, the value of r^n (for $-1 < r < 1$) approaches 0.

2. As n increases without bound, the formula approaches the following expression:

$$S = \frac{g_1 \bullet (0-1)}{r-1} = \frac{g_1 \bullet -1}{r-1} = \frac{g_1}{1-r}$$

h.

1. If $r \leq -1$, $|r^n|$ increases indefinitely as n increases, while r^n alternates between positive and negative values. If $r > 1$, r^n increases indefinitely as n increases.

2. Sample response: The formula is affected in the same manner as r^n.

Assignment

4.1.

a. Sample response: These terms do not appear to have a limit. As the term number increases, the value of the term appears to increase without bound.

b. Sample response: These terms appear to have a limit of 0. As the term number increases, the value of the term approaches 0.

c. Sample response: These terms appear to have a limit of 100 because all the terms are the same.

4.2 Sample spreadsheet:

A	B	C	D	E
1	1		1	
2	10	10	0.1	0.1
3	100	10	0.01	0.1
4	1000	10	0.001	0.1
5	10000	10	0.0001	0.1
6	100000	10	0.00001	0.1
7	1000000	10	0.000001	0.1
8	10000000	10	0.0000001	0.1
9	100000000	10	0.00000001	0.1
10	1000000000	10	1E-09	0.1
⋮	⋮	⋮	⋮	⋮
45	1E+44	10	1E-44	0.1
46	1E+45	10	1E-45	0.1
47	1E+46	10	1E-46	0.1
48	1E+47	10	1E-47	0.1
49	1E+48	10	1E-48	0.1
50	1E+49	10	1E-49	0.1

a. The values in column B are increasing and do not appear to approach a limit. **Note:** Some students may respond that they approach infinity. You may wish to remind them that, although we often talk about positive and negative infinity, infinity is not a real number.

b. The ratio of consecutive terms is 10.

c. The limit of the sequence is 10. After the first term, each successive term is within 0.01 of 10.

d. See sample spreadsheet above.

e. The terms appear to approach 0. After the fifth term, each successive term is within 0.005 of 0.

f. The ratio of consecutive terms is 0.1.

g. The limit of the sequence is 0.1. After the first term, each successive term is within 0.001 of 0.1.

h. **1.** Sample graph:

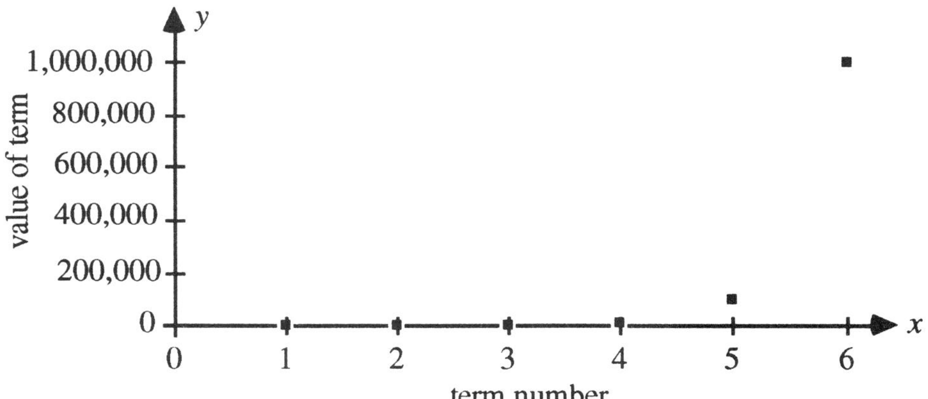

2. Sample graph:

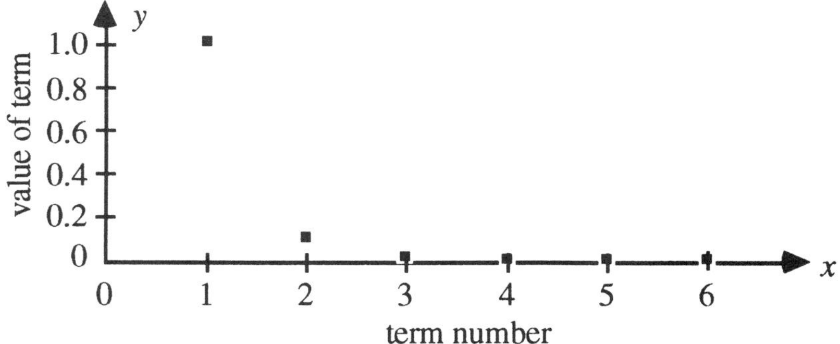

3. Sample response: As the number of terms increases, the scatterplot of column B is increasing and does not approach a limit. As the number of terms increases, the scatterplot of column D is decreasing and appears to approach a limit of 0.

4.3 Sample spreadsheet:

A	B	C	D	E
1	–1		–1	
2	–10	10	–0.1	0.1
3	–100	10	–0.01	0.1
4	–1000	10	–0.001	0.1
5	–10000	10	–0.0001	0.1
6	–100000	10	–0.00001	0.1
7	–1000000	10	–0.000001	0.1
8	–10000000	10	–0.0000001	0.1
9	–100000000	10	–1E-08	0.1
⋮	⋮	⋮	⋮	⋮
48	–1E+47	10	–1E-47	0.1
49	–1E+48	10	–1E-48	0.1
50	–1E+49	10	–1E-49	0.1

a. The terms in column B are decreasing negatively and do not appear to approach a limit.

b. The ratio of consecutive terms is 10.

c. The limit of the sequence is 10. After the first term, all terms are within 0.01 of 10.

d. See sample spreadsheet above.

e. The terms appear to approach 0. After the fourth term, all terms are within 0.005 of 0.

f. The ratio of consecutive terms is 0.1.

g. The limit of the sequence is 0.1. After the first term, all terms are within 0.001 of 0.1.

h. **1.** Sample graph:

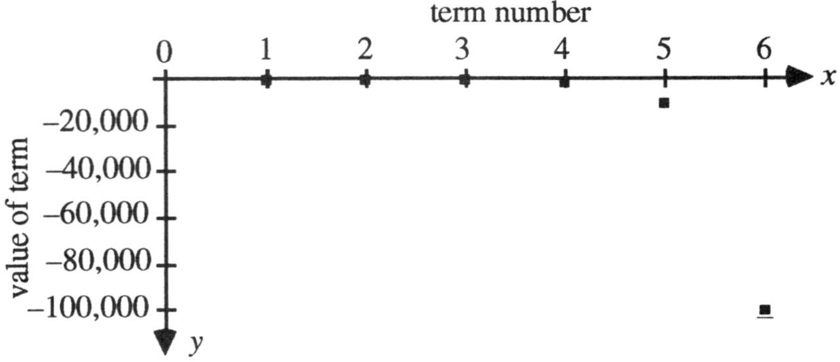

2. Sample graph:

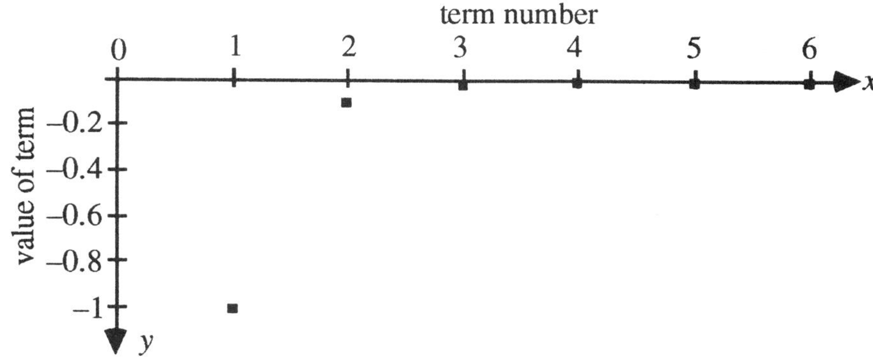

3. Sample response: As the number of terms increases, the scatterplot of column B is decreasing and does not approach a limit. As the number of terms increases, the scatterplot of column D is increasing and appears to approach a limit of 0.

***4.4** In the following sample construction, polygon 1 is *ABEC*, polygon 2 is *GHJK*, polygon 3 is *LMNP* and polygon 4 is *QRST*.

Area(Polygon 1) = 50.28 square cm
Area(Polygon 2) = 25.14 square cm
Area(Polygon 3) = 12.57 square cm
Area(Polygon 4) = 6.29 square cm

Area(Polygon 4)/Area(Polygon 3) = 0.50
Area(Polygon 3)/Area(Polygon 2) = 0.50
Area(Polygon 2)/Area(Polygon 1) = 0.50

Perimeter(Polygon 1) = 28.36 cm
Perimeter(Polygon 2) = 20.06 cm
Perimeter(Polygon 3) = 14.18 cm
Perimeter(Polygon 4) = 10.03 cm

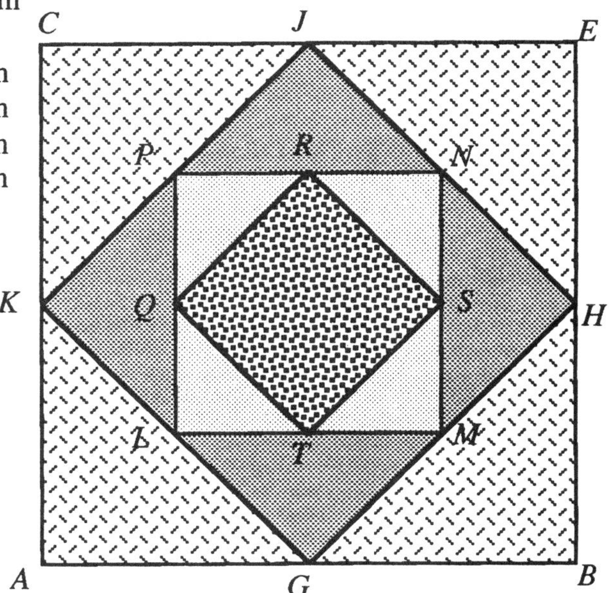

a. Answers may vary. Students should show that the figure is equilateral and that all angles are right angles.

b. Sample response: Each of the other three figures is a square. The four sides of each one are the same length and the four angles in each are right angles.

c–d. Answers will vary, depending on the size of the original square.

e. 1. Students should observe that the ratio of consecutive areas is $1/2$.

2. The ratio of the areas of consecutive squares is not the same as the ratios of the areas of the consecutive triangles.

f. Sample response: The ratio of the perimeters is $\sqrt{2}/2 \approx 0.707$, which is not the same as the ratios of the perimeters for the triangles.

g. 1. The sequence of areas approaches 0.

2. The sequence of perimeters approaches 0.

4.5 Since $r = 0.2$ and $g_1 = 98$, the sum can be found as follows:

$$S = \frac{98}{1-0.2} = 122.5$$

* * * * *

4.6 **a.** Sample response: [3, 4], [3, 3.5], [3, $3.\overline{3}$], [3, 3.25].

b. Sample response: As *n* increases, the limit appears to be the interval [3, 3], which is equivalent to 3.

4.7 **a.** $r = 1/10$

b. The limit of the sequence appears to be 0.

c. After the third term, all the following terms are within 0.001 of 0.

d. $\frac{6}{10}, \frac{66}{100}, \frac{666}{1000}, \frac{6666}{10{,}000}, \frac{66{,}666}{100{,}000}, \frac{666{,}666}{1{,}000{,}000}$

e. The limit of the sequence of sums appears to be $2/3$. **Note:** You may wish to discuss other infinitely repeating decimals whose limits are exact values, such as $0.3\overline{3} = 1/3$.

4.8 Students may wish to use a spreadsheet to investigate this situation.

a. 250, $250 + 0.10(250)$, $250 + 0.10(250 + 0.10(250))$, $250 + 0.10(250 + 0.10(250 + 0.10(250)))$ or 250, 275, 277.5, 277.75

b. 277.5 mg

c–d. Sample response: By the middle of the third day (after five tablets), the amount of medication in the body approaches a limit of approximately 277.8 mg.

Number of Tablets	Amount of Medication in Body (mg)
0	250
1	275
2	277.5
3	277.75
4	277.775
5	277.7775
6	277.778
7	277.778
8	277.778

4.9 $\dfrac{5}{11} = 0.\overline{45} = \dfrac{45}{100} + \dfrac{45}{10,000} + \dfrac{45}{1,000,000} + \cdots$

4.10 **a.** $g_1 = 0.27,\ g_2 = 0.0027,\ g_3 = 0.000027,\ g_4 = 0.00000027$

b. The sum of the infinite geometric sequence can be found as follows:

$$S = \frac{0.27}{1-0.01} = \frac{0.27}{0.99} = \frac{27}{99} = \frac{3}{11}$$

* * * * * * * * * *

Research Project

a. One good resource for students is Peitgen, et al., *Fractals for the Classroom.* The authors provide many references to Sierpinski and describes how to produce these triangles using graphing calculators or dot paper.

b. When students construct these figures, they should observe that the first quadrilateral is a parallelogram (a rhombus), but not a rectangle. The second quadrilateral is a rectangle. This alternating pattern continues. The ratio of the areas of consecutive rectangles is a constant, while the ratio of the areas of consecutive parallelograms is a different constant.

Answers to Summary Assessment

1. Students may use different methods to analyze this situation. The area added to the snowflake at each stage after stage 1 can be described by the geometric sequence below, where n is the stage number minus 1:

$$\frac{3}{9}, \frac{3}{9}\left(\frac{4}{9}\right), \frac{3}{9}\left(\frac{4}{9}\right)^2, \ldots, \frac{3}{9}\left(\frac{4}{9}\right)^{n-1}$$

Thus, the area of the snowflake at each stage is:

$$1+S_n = 1+\frac{3}{9}+\frac{3}{9}\left(\frac{4}{9}\right)+\frac{3}{9}\left(\frac{4}{9}\right)^2+\cdots+\frac{3}{9}\left(\frac{4}{9}\right)^{n-1}$$

a. 1 unit^2

b. Using the expression shown above, where n is the stage number minus 1:

$$1+S_1 = 1+\frac{3}{9} = 1\tfrac{1}{3} \text{ units}^2$$

c. By combining the expression shown above, where n is the stage number minus 1, with the formula for an infinite geometric series in which $-1<r<1$:

$$1+S_{14} = 1+\frac{\left(\frac{3}{9}\right)\left(\frac{4}{9}\right)^{14}-\frac{3}{9}}{\frac{4}{9}-1} \approx 1.60 \text{ units}^2$$

2. Sample response: The area of the snowflake approaches 1.6 units^2. The following graph shows how, after stage 5, all of the terms fall within 0.05 units of 1.6.

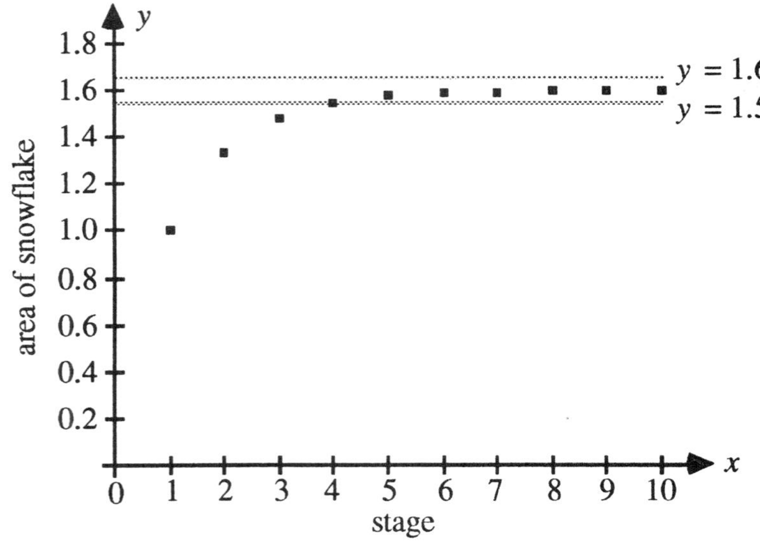

Module Assessment

1. a. Consider an arithmetic sequence in which the 1st term is –4 and the 11th term is –38.

    1. What is the common difference?

    2. What are the intermediate 9 terms?

    3. What is the sum of the first 11 terms?

   b. Consider a geometric sequence in which the 1st term is –4 and the 6th term is 128.

    1. What is the common ratio?

    2. What are the intermediate four terms?

    3. What is the sum of the first 20 terms?

2. In Problem **1.6**, you examined the claims of a veterinary diet that promised to "help your pet lose 0.9 kg a month."

   a. If that claim is true, a pet's continued loss of mass could be represented by a finite arithmetic sequence. How many terms could be in the sequence? Explain your response.

   b. Imagine that the ad promised a pet could lose 1 kg the first month, 0.5 kg the second month, 0.25 kg the third month, and so on. If that claim were true, a pet's continued loss of mass could be represented by a finite geometric sequence. What is the common ratio of this sequence? Explain your response.

   c. Could the continued loss of the pet's mass be represented by an infinite geometric sequence? Explain your response.

3. The sequence 1, 3, 4, 7, 11, 18, 29, 47, 76, ... is credited to the French mathematician Edouard Lucas.

   a. Write the next five terms in the sequence.

   b. Determine whether the sequence is arithmetic, geometric, or neither.

   c. Write a recursive formula for the sequence.

4. a. Write an explicit formula for a geometric sequence with a common ratio of 0.5 and a first term of 40.

   b. Create a graph of the first 15 terms of the sequence.

   c. If this sequence continued indefinitely, would it approach a limit?

   d. Find the sum of the first 15 terms of the sequence.

Answers to Module Assessment

1\. a. 1. The common difference is –3.4.

2\. The intermediate terms are –7.4, –10.8, –14.2, –17.6, –21, –24.4, –27.8, –31.2, and –34.6.

3\. The sum of the first 11 terms can be found as follows:

$$S_{11} = \frac{11}{2}(-4 + (-38)) = -231$$

b. 1. The common ratio is –2.

2\. The intermediate terms are 8, –16, 32, and –64.

3\. The sum of the first 20 terms can be found as follows:

$$S_{20} = \frac{-4(-2)^{20} - (-4)}{-2 - 1} = 1{,}398{,}100$$

2\. a. Answers will vary. Sample response: If represented as a sequence, the pet's continued mass loss cannot have more than a few terms. Unless the pet is extremely overweight, it should not take more than a few months to reach a healthy level. Taken literally, losing mass continually at 0.9 kg per month means that a 20-kg dog would have no mass at the end of 22 months.

b. Sample response: If the claim is true, it's possible that a pet's mass loss could be represented by a finite geometric sequence with a first term of 1 and a common ratio of 0.5.

c. Sample response: The geometric sequence 1, 0.5, 0.25, … appears to approach a limit of 0. The corresponding series appears to approach a limit of 2. It might be possible for a pet to lose mass according to this geometric sequence—whether finite or infinite. Continuing the pattern, the total mass loss would never be more than 2 kg.

3\. a. The next five terms are 123, 199, 322, 521, 843.

b. The sequence is neither arithmetic nor geometric because it has neither a common difference nor a common ratio.

c. Sample response:

$$\begin{cases} p_1 = 1 \\ p_2 = 3 \\ p_n = p_{n-1} + p_{n-2}, \quad n > 2 \end{cases}$$

4. **a.** The explicit formula is $g_n = 40 \bullet (0.5)^{n-1}$.

b. Sample graph:

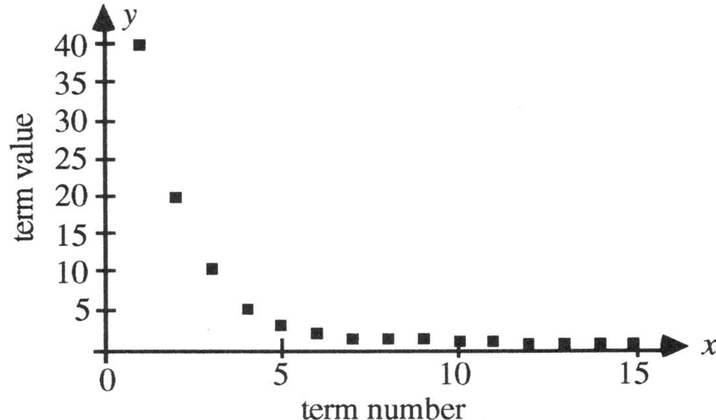

c. As n increases, the terms appear to approach 0.

d. Using the formula for the sum of a geometric series:

$$S_n = \frac{g_1 r^n - g_1}{r-1} = \frac{40(0.5)^{15} - 40}{0.5-1} \approx 80$$

Selected References

Bennett, Jr., A. B. "Visualizing the Geometric Series." *Mathematics Teacher* 82 (February 1989): 130–36.

Buchanan, O. L. *Limits: A Transition to Calculus.* Boston: Houghton Mifflin, 1985.

Garland, T. H. *Fascinating Fibonaccis: Mystery and Magic in Numbers.* Palo Alto: Dale Seymour Publications, 1987.

Huntley, H. E. *The Divine Proportion: A Study in Mathematical Beauty.* New York: Dover Publications, 1970.

Peitgen, H.-O., H. Jürgens, D. Saupe, E. Maletsky, T. Perciante, and L. Yunker. *Fractals for the Classroom.* New York: Springer-Verlag, 1991.

Flashbacks

Activity 1

1.1 Find a possible next term for each of the following sequences.

a. 10, 5, 0, –5, …

b. $\frac{1}{2}, \frac{7}{6}, \frac{11}{6}, \frac{5}{2}, \ldots$

1.2 Consider the following arithmetic sequence:

$$-2, -5.4, -8.8, \ldots, -53$$

a. What is the common difference?

b. How many terms are in the sequence?

1.3 If a_n describes any term in a sequence, which terms are described by each of the following notations?

a. a_{n+1}

b. a_{n-1}

1.4 Write the first three terms of the sequence defined by the formula below:

$$x_n = 2(n-1)^{n+1}$$

Activity 2

2.1 What is the sum of the first 10 natural numbers?

2.2 Write both an explicit and a recursive formula for each of the following sequences:

a. 8, 16, 24, 32, ...

b. 1, 4, 16, 64, ...

2.3 Consider the following geometric sequence:

$$5, -15, 45, \ldots, -10{,}935$$

a. What is the common ratio?

b. How many terms are in the sequence?

Activity 3

3.1 Simplify each of the following expressions:

a. $x \bullet x^n$

b. $x \bullet x^{n-1}$

c. $x \bullet x^{n-2}$

3.2 Multiply both sides of the equation below by x:

$$A = b + bx + bx^2 + bx^3 + \cdots + bx^{m-2} + bx^{m-1}$$

3.3 Solve the following equation for x:

$$ax + bx = 12$$

3.4 Find the sum of the arithmetic series below:

$$6,\ 8,\ 10,\ 12,\ \ldots,\ 52$$

Activity 4

4.1 Consider a geometric sequence in which $g_1 = 8/3$ and $r = 1/2$. What is the sum of the first 5 terms of this sequence?

4.2 Consider an arithmetic sequence in which $a_1 = 8/3$ and $d = 1/2$. What is the sum of the first 5 terms of this sequence?

4.3 Is there an integer n for which $1/n = 0$? Explain your response.

Answers to Flashbacks

Activity 1

1.1 **a.** Answers may vary. Sample response: –10.

b. Answers may vary. Sample response: 19/6.

1.2 **a.** The common difference is –3.4.

b. The number of terms can be found as follows:

$$-53 = -2 + (n-1) \bullet -3.4$$
$$n = \frac{-53+2}{-3.4} + 1$$
$$= 16$$

1.3 **a.** Sample response: The term a_{n+1} is the term following a_n.

b. Sample response: The term a_{n-1} is the term before a_n.

1.4 0, 2, 32

Activity 2

2.1 The sum of the first 10 natural numbers is 55.

2.2 **a.** One possible explicit formula is $a_n = 8 + 8(n-1)$ for $n \geq 1$. A possible recursive formula is shown below:

$$\begin{cases} a_1 = 8 \\ a_n = a_{n-1} + 8 \text{ for } n > 1 \end{cases}$$

b. One possible explicit formula is $g_n = 1(4)^{n-1}$ for $n \geq 1$. A possible recursive formula is shown below:

$$\begin{cases} g_1 = 1 \\ g_n = 4g_{n-1} \text{ for } n > 1 \end{cases}$$

2.3 **a.** The common ratio is –3.

b. The number of terms can be found as follows:

$$-10{,}935 = 5(-3)^{n-1}$$
$$\frac{-10{,}935}{5} = (-3)^{n-1}$$
$$n = 8$$

Activity 3

3.1 **a.** $x \bullet x^n = x^{n+1}$

b. $x \bullet x^{n-1} = x^n$

c. $x \bullet x^{n-2} = x^{n-1}$

3.2 $xA = bx + bx^2 + bx^3 + bx^4 + \cdots + bx^{m-1} + bx^m$

3.3 Sample response:

$$x(a+b) = 12$$
$$x = \frac{12}{a+b}$$

3.4 The number of terms can be found as follows:

$$52 = 6 + (n-1) \bullet 2$$
$$n = \frac{52-6}{2} + 1$$
$$= 24$$

Using the formula for a finite arithmetic series:

$$S_{24} = \frac{24}{2}(6+52) = 696$$

Activity 4

4.1 Using the formula for a finite geometric series:

$$S_5 = \frac{\frac{8}{3}\left(\frac{1}{2}^5 - 1\right)}{\frac{1}{2} - 1} = \frac{31}{6} \approx 5.16$$

4.2 Using the formula for a finite arithmetic series:

$$S_5 = \frac{5}{2}\left(2 \bullet \frac{8}{3} + (5-1) \bullet \frac{1}{2}\right) = \frac{55}{3} \approx 18.3$$

4.3 Sample response: No. If $1/n = 0$, then $1 = n \bullet 0$. This cannot be true.

Algorithmic Thinking

What do baking a cake, programming a VCR, and adding a pair of two-digit numbers have in common? In this module, you explore how algorithms affect everything from cooking to computers.

Wendy Driscoll • Darlene Pugh • Todd Robins

Teacher Edition
Algorithmic Thinking

Overview

In this module, students examine some classic algorithms, create flowcharts, and use recursion in algorithms.

Objectives

In this module, students will:

- construct algorithms
- use algorithmic thinking
- examine the efficiency of algorithms
- organize algorithms into flowcharts
- develop algorithms that use recursion.

Prerequisites

For this module, students should know:

- the definition of prime numbers
- how to write recursive formulas of sequences.

Time Line

Activity	1	2	3	Summary Assessment	Total
Days	2	3	3	1	9

Materials Required

Materials	Activity			
	1	2	3	Summary Assessment
compass	X			
ruler	X			
protractor	X			
flowchart template		X		
scissors		X		
tape or glue		X		

Teacher Note

A blackline master of the template appears at the end of this teacher edition.

Technology

Software	Activity			
	1	2	3	Summary Assessment
geometry utility			X	

Algorithmic Thinking

Introduction

Students may recall the definition of an algorithm from the Level 1 module "Going in Circuits." The historical note describes the derivation of the word from the name of an Arabian mathematician, Mohammed ibn-Musa al-Khwarizmi. (The title of another of al-Khwarizmi's influential works, *Al-jabr wa'l muqabalah*, is the source of the word *algebra*.)

Activity 1

Students investigate some characteristics desirable in algorithms.

Materials List

- compass (one per student)
- ruler (one per student)
- protractor (one per student)

Exploration

Students experiment with writing clear and efficient algorithms.

a. You may wish to encourage students to keep the pictures simple.

b. Student instructions may appear in a list, as a paragraph, or in other forms.

c–d. Each student should follow the partner's instructions exactly as written, without additions or omissions.

e. Students revise their algorithms based on the results of Part **d**.

f. The revised algorithms may be more efficient.

Discussion

a. Answers will vary. In most cases, the two pictures are likely to look somewhat different.

b–c. The simplest pictures—with the most concise instructions—should take the least amount of time to reproduce. A drawing of three concentric circles of specified radii, for example, should be fairly easy to duplicate.

d. Answers will vary. Some students will consider only time when determining efficiency. (This is also the typical measure of efficiency in computer programming.) Others may consider the quality of the writing and the accuracy of the recreated picture as part of the "efficiency" of a set of instructions.

e. Sample response: Yes, it is possible to have more than one set of instructions for the same picture. For example, the two instructions "draw an equilateral triangle with side length of 5 cm" and "draw an equiangular triangle whose sides are 5 cm long" both produce the same figure.

f. Students should reflect on the characteristics of clear, easy-to-follow instructions. Eliminating trivial steps, ordering the steps numerically, and using vocabulary appropriate for the audience all may be factors in making instructions more clear.

g. Sample response: The vocabulary may need to change. For example, an elementary student may not know the meaning of "regular heptagon."

Assignment

1.1 **a.** Sample response for washing clothes: Jillian packed the machine full of white cotton shirts, then added a red silk blouse. The load indicator was set on "small," but she did not adjust it. She poured in half a box of soap, then turned on the machine. Complete disaster!

Sample response for preparing a bath: Jack set the water temperature just right, put the towels by the tub, and sat down to wait. Since he had neglected to put in the plug, however, the tub never filled.

b. Sample response for washing clothes: The instructions do not represent a successful algorithm because they are not precise. The instructions should include directions for sorting clothes by color and fabric, and for setting water temperature, load size, and wash cycle (like permanent press, for example). They should also specify the amount of soap needed.

Sample response for preparing a bath: The instructions are for a task that will not terminate. As written, the instructions do not direct the person to close the drain—or tell when to turn off the water.

c. Sample response:

Washing Clothes
Sort the clothes into light or dark.
If the clothes are light, set the machine on hot or warm.
If the clothes are dark, set the machine on cool or cold.
Add one scoop of soap.
Add the clothes, but do not overfill the washer.
Select the load size and wash cycle.
Start the machine.

1.2 **a.** Sample response: This recipe will probably not always produce the same results. A difference in the amount of milk may change the consistency of the dough. And different cooks will have different ideas of what is "warm." The variations in temperature may cause the yeast to act differently. The temperature of the hot grease will also affect the bread.

b. Sample response: There are many decisions points in this recipe. For example, "Beat until smooth" demands a decision on the meaning of smoothness. Also "turning the bread until golden brown" creates another decision to be made. In the first case, if the dough is not smooth enough, the bread will have lumps. In the second case, what looks like golden brown to some may mean overcooked—or burned—to others.

1.3 **a.** The first 20 prime numbers are 2, 3, 5, 7, 11, 13, 17, 19, 23, 29, 31, 37, 41, 43, 47, 53, 59, 61, 67, and 71.

b. Sample response: If the number is 1 or the number is divisible by any natural number less than itself (but greater than 1), then it is not prime. Otherwise it is prime.

***1.4** **a.** Sample response:

1. Subtract the cost of the item from 100 cents.
2. Divide the difference in step 1 by 25 cents.
3. The integer part of the quotient in step 2 is the number of quarters in change.
4. Divide the remainder of the quotient in step 2 by 10 cents.
5. The integer part of the quotient in step 4 is the number of dimes in change.
6. Divide the remainder of the quotient in step 4 by 5 cents.
7. The integer part of the quotient in step 6 is the number of nickels in change.
8. The remainder of the quotient in step 6 is the number of pennies in change.

b. The following sample response uses an item which costs \$0.33.

1. $100 - 33 = 67$
2. $67/25 = 2$, remainder 17
3. There are two quarters in change.
4. $17/10 = 1$, remainder 7
5. There is one dime in change.
6. $7/5 = 1$, remainder 2
7. There is one nickel in change.
8. There are two pennies in change.

c. The sample algorithm given in Part **a** requires a knowledge of the arithmetic terms *product*, *quotient*, *remainder*, and *integer part.*

* * * * *

1.5 a. Students should substitute and solve as shown below:

$$C = \frac{5}{9}(99 - 32) \approx 37^\circ$$

b. The following algorithm will convert temperature in degrees Celsius to degrees Fahrenheit.

- Let F represent the temperature in degrees Fahrenheit and C the temperature in degrees Celsius.
- Substitute the value of C into the following equation.

$$F = \frac{9}{5}C + 32$$

- Solve the equation for F.

1.6 a. Sample response: It would trace an equilateral triangle with sides 10 m long.

b. Sample response:

- Forward(x)
- Right(90°)
- Forward(x)
- Right(90°)
- Forward(x)
- Right(90°)
- Forward(x)
- Right(90°)

c. Answers will vary. Students create an algorithm that will trace a figure and ask another student to follow the algorithm.

* * * * * * * * * *

Activity 2

In this activity, students create flowcharts for algorithms.

Materials List

- flowchart template (one copy per student; a blackline master appears at the end of this teacher edition)
- scissors (one pair per student)
- tape or glue

Exploration 1

a–b. Students organize the command boxes on the flowchart template into a usable order and draw the appropriate arrows. Sample response:

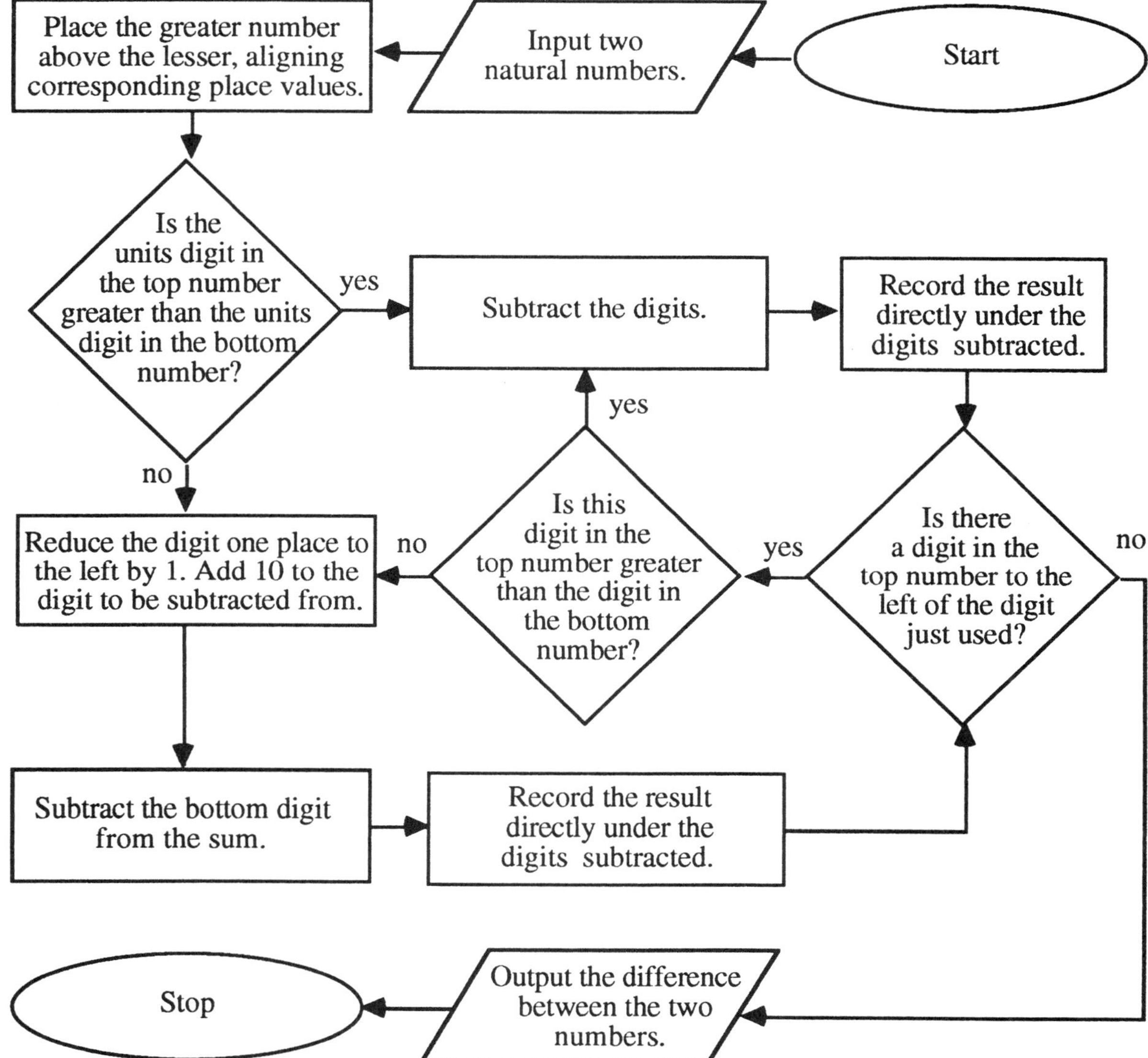

c. After exchanging flowcharts, students should test the algorithm using two natural numbers.

Discussion 1

a. Sample response: No. Although the order is basically the same in all of the flowcharts, the arrangement of the command boxes on the page varies.

b. Sample response: I placed the start command at the beginning and the input command next. Then I looked for a processing box that seemed to describe the first step in the subtraction algorithm. After that, I tested each command box to see if it contained the following step.

c. Sample response: To make the flowchart easier to read, the command boxes should be lined up (when possible) and the arrows should be clearly drawn.

Exploration 2

Students write an algorithm for adding a pair of two-digit numbers and draw the corresponding flowchart.

a. Students may select any pair of two-digit numbers. The sum of 84 and 39 is 123.

b. Sample response:

1. Add the units digits of the pair of numbers. In this case, $4+9=13$.
2. If the sum of the units digits is greater than 10, separate the sum into two parts, 10 and the rest. If not, the sum of the units digits is the units digit of the final sum. In this case, separate the sum into 10 and 3.
3. Add the tens digits of the pair of numbers. In this case, $8+3=11$.
4. Add the sum of the tens digits and the number of 10s from the sum of the units digits. If the number is less than 10, this is the tens digit of the final sum. In this case, $11+1=12$.
5. If the number is more than 10, then separate this sum into 10 tens and the rest. In this case, separate the sum into 10 and 2. The number of 10 tens becomes the hundreds digit of the final sum; the remainder becomes the tens digit in the final sum. In this case, the hundreds digit is 1 and the tens digit is 2.
6. The sum of the two original numbers has a hundreds digit (if any) from Step 5, a tens digit from Step 4 or Step 5, and a units digit from Step 2. In this case, the sum is 123.

c. Students should use the flowchart symbols from Figure **1**. See sample flowchart given in Part **e**.

d. Students exchange flowcharts and test their partners' instructions.

e. Sample flowchart:

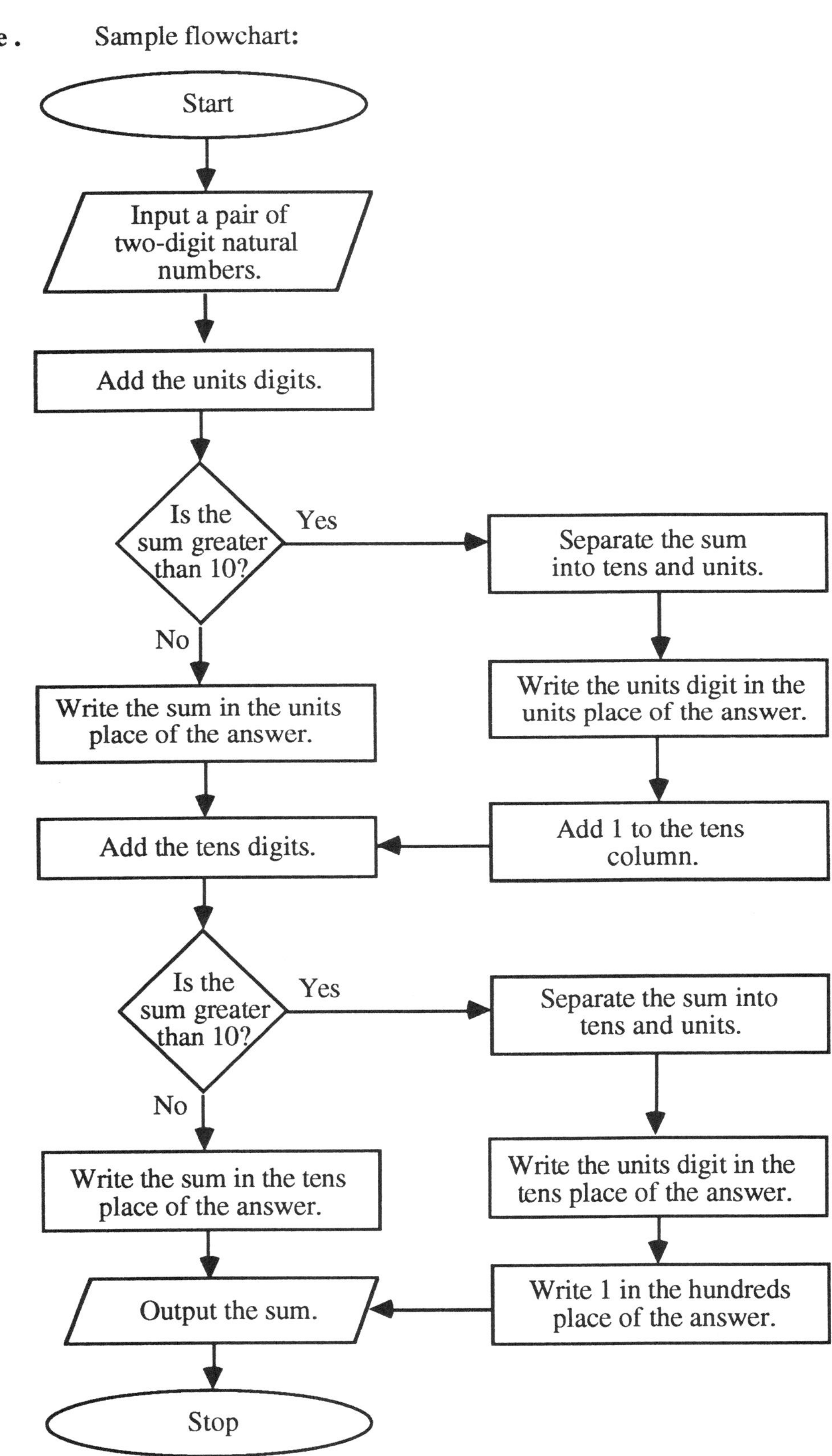

Discussion 2

a. Students should compare the sequence and organization of the steps in their algorithms, as well as the use of flowchart symbols.

b. When evaluating flowcharts, students may consider precision, ease of interpretation, and time required to complete the algorithm.

c. Sample response: The flowchart could be extended to find the sum of a pair of three-digit numbers by including boxes to find the sum of the hundreds digits and to determine whether or not the sum contains 10 hundreds to see how many thousands (if any) are in the sum.

Assignment

2.1 **a.** **1.** \$367.50

2. \$270.00

b. Sample flowchart:

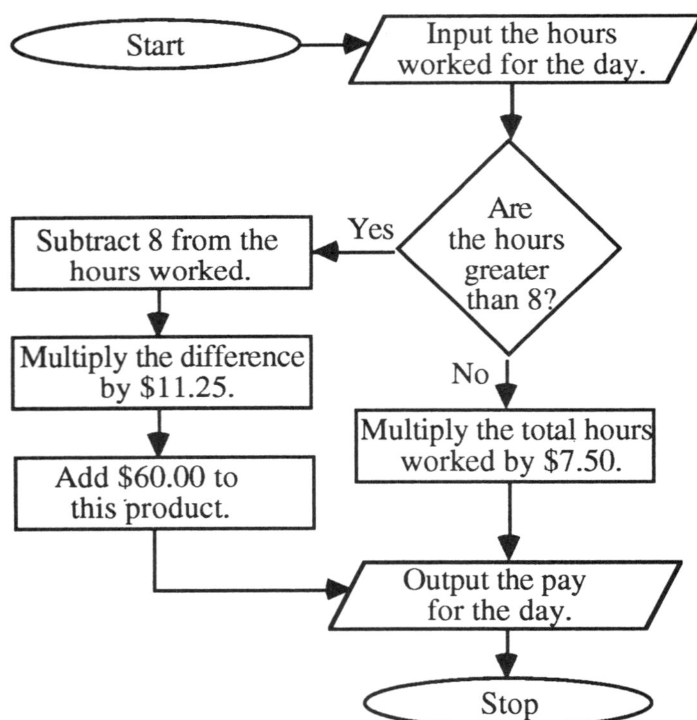

c. Sample response: Company B would be better to work for because it pays overtime whenever an employee works more than 8 hours in 1 day. For example, an employee who worked 11 hours on 1 day of the week and 7 hours on each of the remaining 4 days would get paid \$303.75 if she worked for Company B, but only \$292.50 if she worked for Company A.

2.2 Sample flowchart:

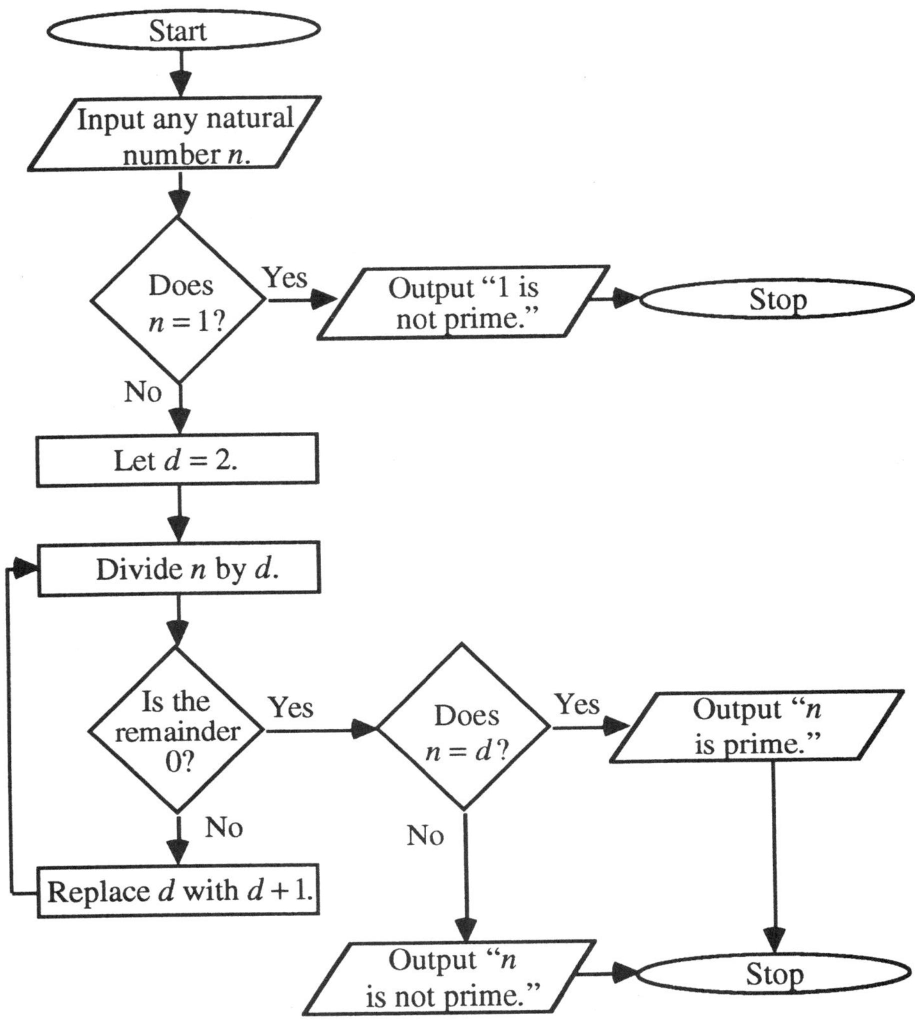

2.3

a. By playing the game several times, students should recognize that a winning algorithm exists.

b. Sample response: The winning algorithm is to allow your partner to play first and control the sum at the end of each round. If your partner plays 1, then you should play 2 to keep the total for the round at 3. If your partner plays 2, then you should play 1. By playing second and continuing to force the total to be a multiple of 3, the total after 7 rounds will be 21 and you will win.

c. Sample response: You could program a computer to win at this game if the human player always goes first. The program would have to instruct the computer to play a 2 every time its opponent played a 1, and a 1 every time its opponent played a 2.

*2.4 **a.** The insert sort algorithm requires 28 comparisons to sort this list of 10 numbers.

b. Sample flowchart:

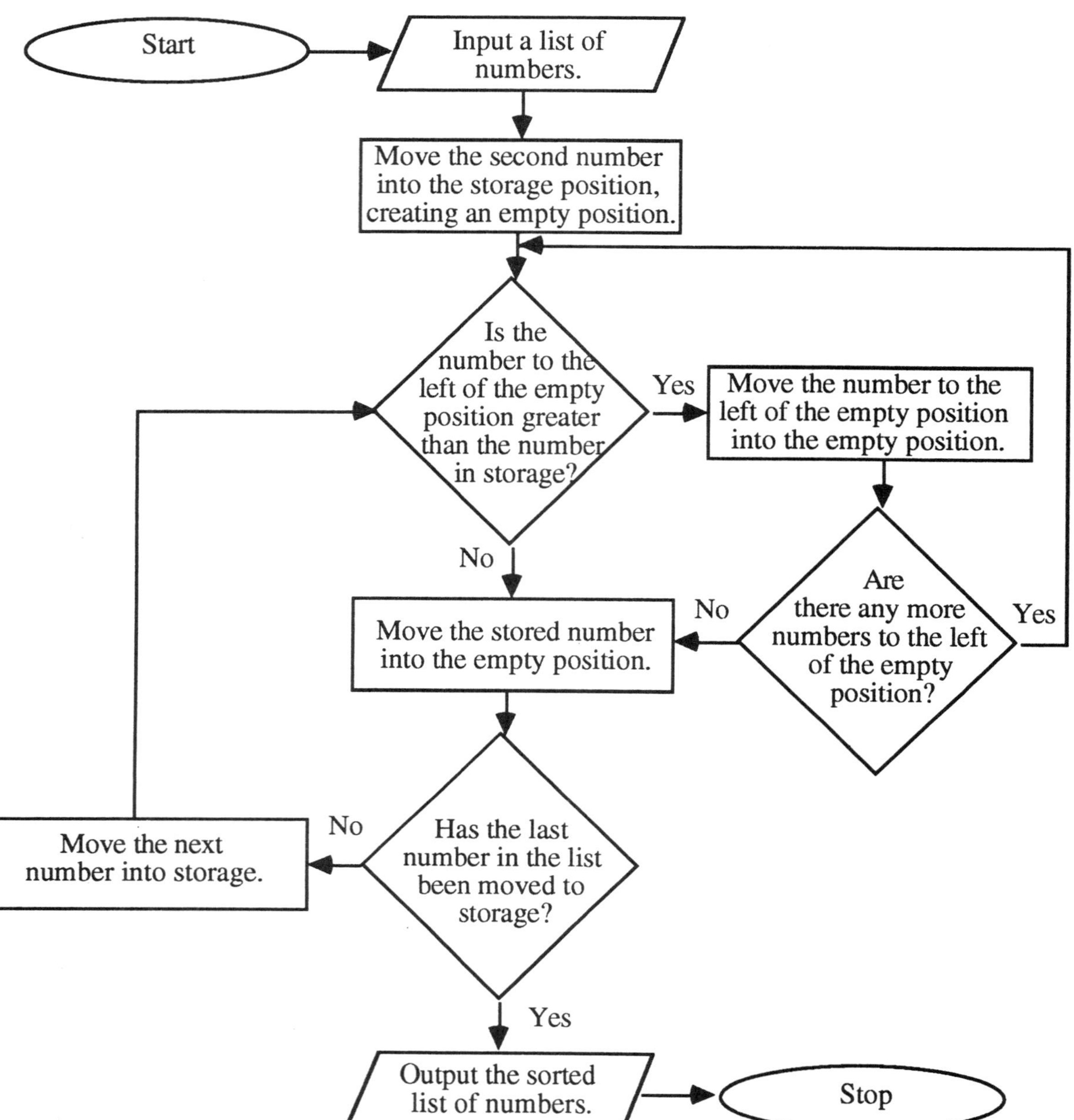

c. Sample response: The merge sort appears to be the most efficient, since it takes 4 fewer comparisons than the insertion sort and 21 fewer comparisons than the bubble sort.

2.5 Sample flowchart:

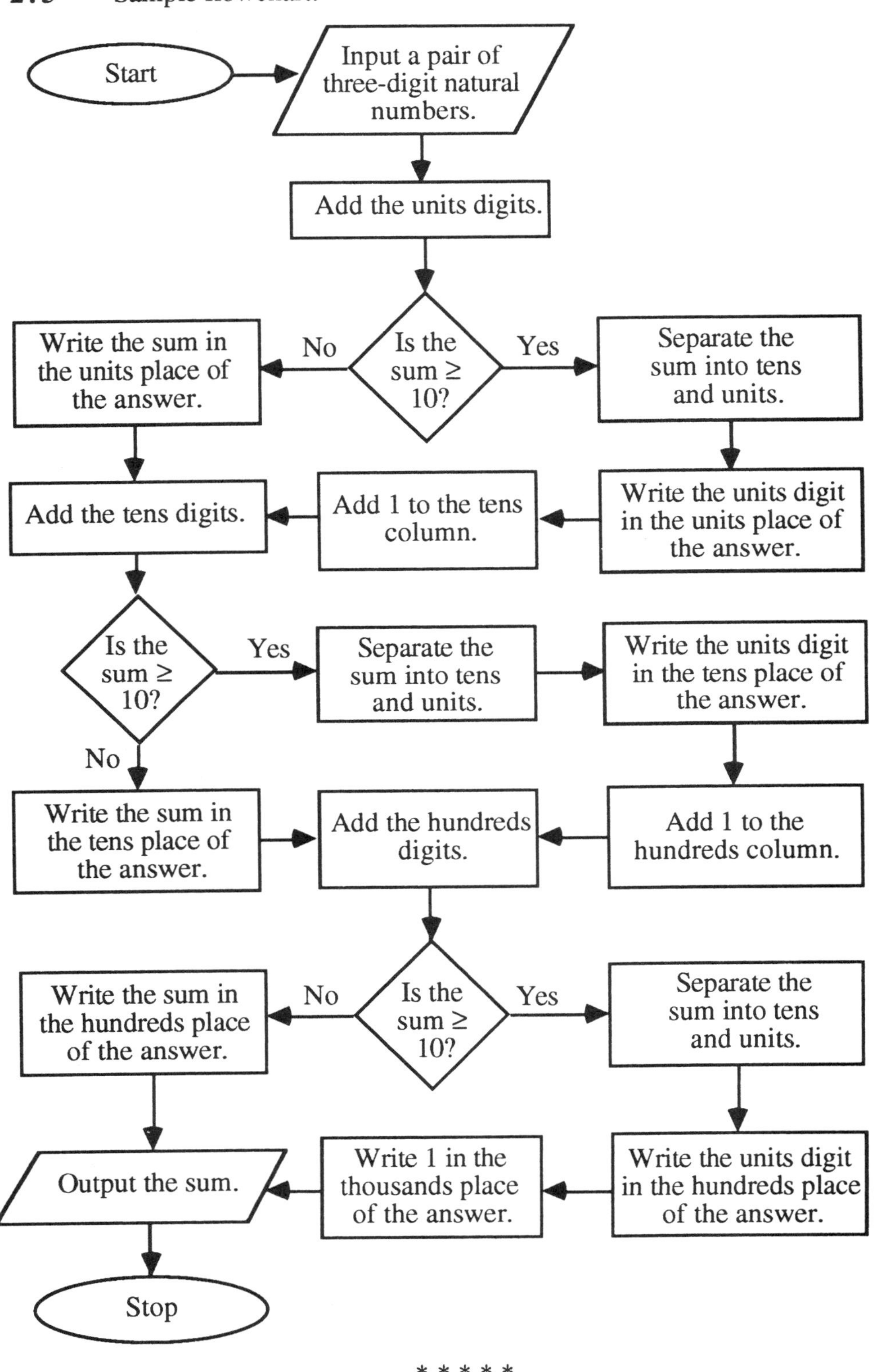

* * * * *

2.6 Sample flowchart:

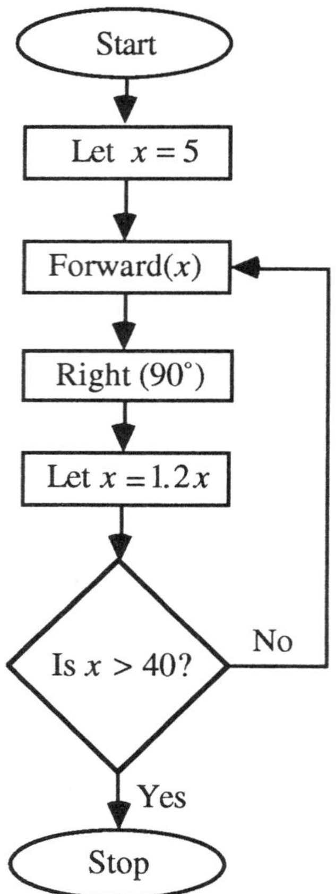

Teacher Note

The algorithm described in Problem **2.7** relies on the fact that the greatest common divisor of two natural numbers a and b is the same as the greatest common divisor of a and $b-a$. In other words, $\gcd(a,b) = \gcd(a,b-a)$. This may be proved as follows:

Let $d = \gcd(a,b)$. This means that d divides a or that there is an integer n such that $dn = a$. This also means that d divides b or that there is an integer m such that $dm = b$. Furthermore, d is the greatest integer that divides both a and b. Because $dn = a$ and $dm = b$, then $dm - dn = b - a$. Thus $d(m-n) = b-a$, so d divides $b-a$.

Suppose that an integer $x = \gcd(a,b-a)$. This means that x is the greatest integer that divides both a and $b-a$. This implies that $xy = a$ and $xz = b-a$ for some integers y and z. Thus, $xz + xy = b - a + a$ and $x(z+y) = b$. Thus x divides b. Now x divides both a and b, but x must be less than d. This contradicts the assumption that $x = \gcd(a,b-a)$, since d is greater than x and divides both.

Therefore, $d = \gcd(a,b-a)$ and $\gcd(a,b) = \gcd(a,b-a)$.

2.7 **a.** **1.** 6

2. 3

3. 1

b. Sample flowchart:

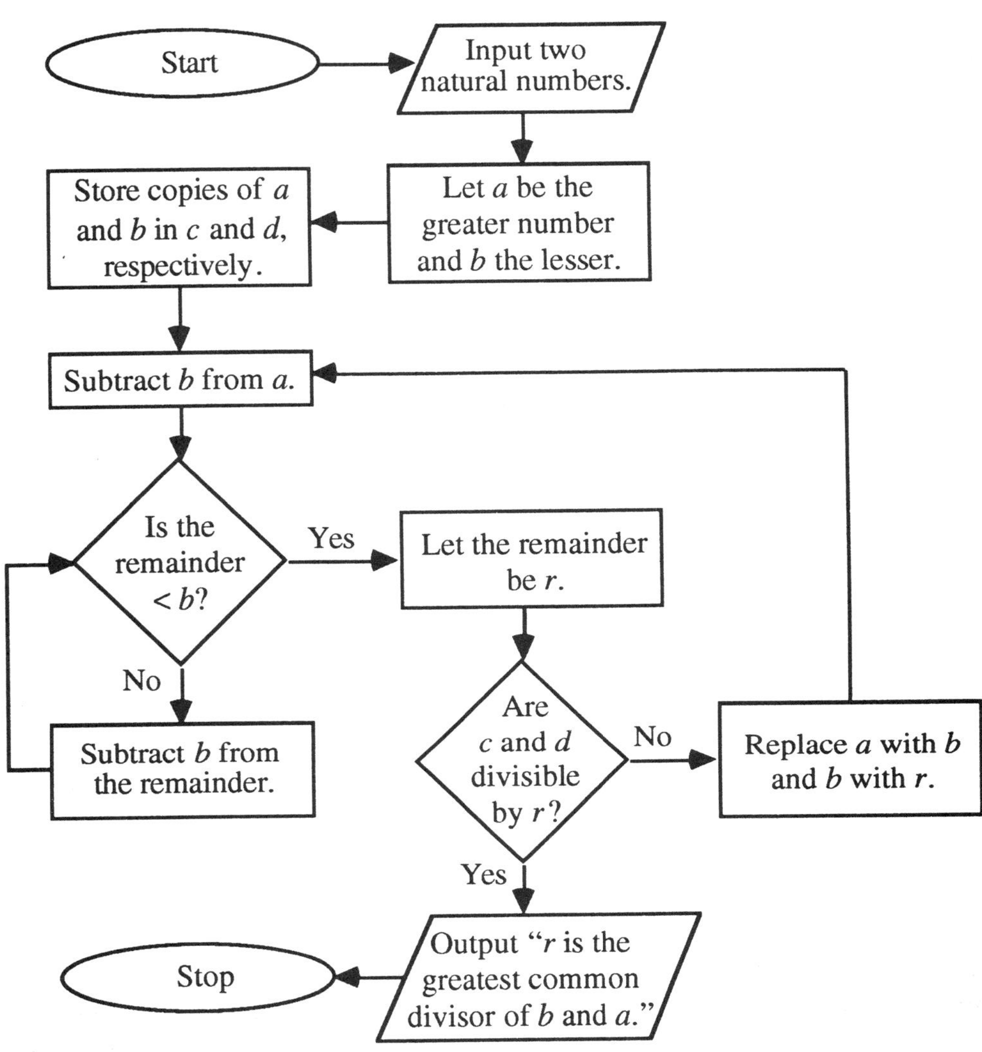

c. Sample response: Yes, the Euclidean algorithm could be adapted to find the greatest common divisor of any two integers. This is because the greatest common divisor of a and b, $-a$ and b, a and $-b$, and $-a$ and $-b$ are all equal.

2.8 **a.** Sample response: The Euclidean algorithm consists of a process for finding the greatest common divisor of two natural numbers. To do this using division, divide the greater number by the lesser and consider the remainder. If the remainder is 0, then the divisor is the greatest common divisor of the two numbers. If not, then divide the previous divisor by the remainder and consider the new remainder as described above. Repeat the process until the remainder is 0. The greatest common divisor of the two original numbers is the divisor when the remainder is 0.

b. Sample flowchart:

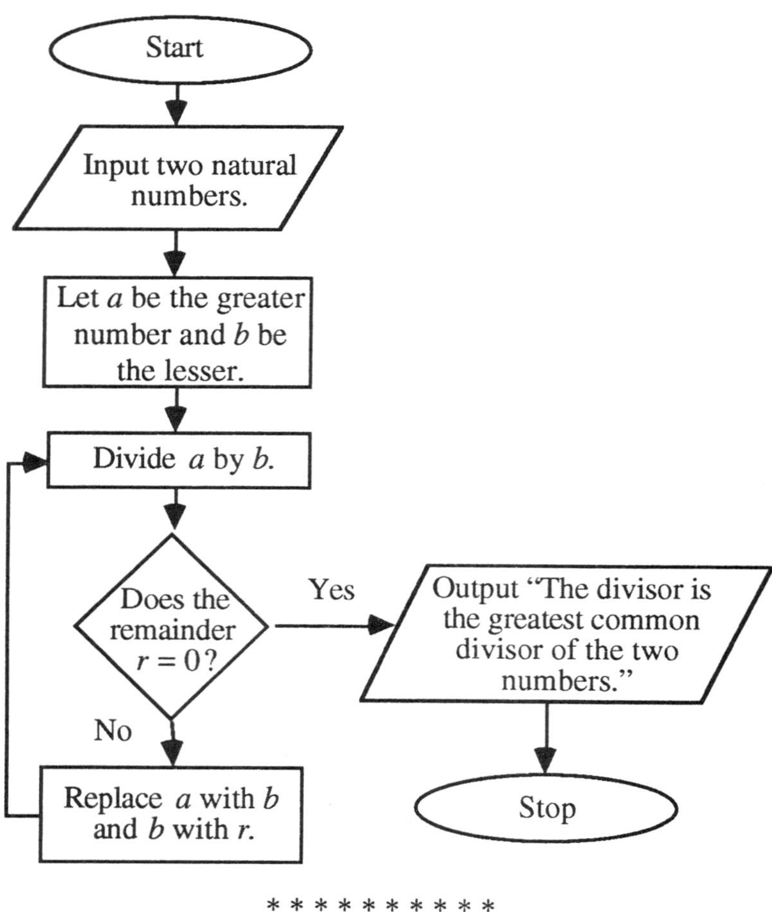

* * * * * * * * * *

Research Project

There are many variations of Nim. Using 1 and n, where n is a natural number, and a target number T, where T is a multiple of $1+n$, the sum can be controlled by the second player as described in Problem **2.3**.

If T is not a multiple of $1+n$, then the first player can control the game by using the first turn to reduce the remaining sum to a multiple of $1+n$, then continuing to keep the remaining sum a multiple of $1+n$.

Activity 3

Students explore the use of recursion in algorithms involving geometric figures.

Materials List

- none

Technology

- geometry utility

Exploration

Students use recursive algorithms to create geometric shapes.

a. Sample construction:

b. Sample algorithm:

Given:	A square.
Procedure:	1. Make a copy of the polygon. 2. Locate the new polygon so that its center coincides with the center of the original polygon. 3. Dilate the new polygon by a scale factor of 0.8 with center of dilation at the center of the polygon. 4. Rotate the new polygon clockwise until it is inscribed in the previous polygon. 5. Repeat the procedure on the new polygon.

c. Sample construction:

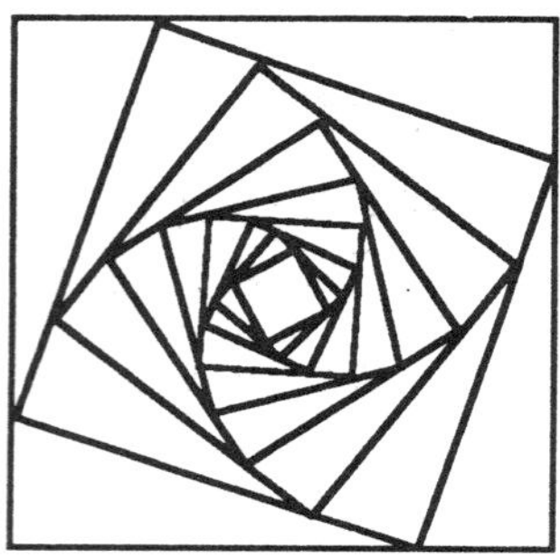

Discussion

a. The procedure $a_n = a_{n-1} + 7$ creates recursion.

b. In the algorithm described in Table **1**, step 3 creates recursion.

c. The limit of the perimeters of the inscribed polygons is 0.

d.
1. Sample response: Change step 3 to read: "Repeat the procedure 9 times."
2. Sample response: Change the given information to "a quadrilateral."

Assignment

3.1
a. The first five terms are 3, 12, 48, 192, 768.

b. The given information is $g_1 = 3$.

c. The procedure is defined by $g_n = 4g_{n-1}$.

***3.2** Sample algorithm.

Given:	A pentagon.
Procedure:	1. Make a copy of the polygon to create a new polygon. 2. Locate the new polygon so that its center coincides with the center of the original polygon. 3. Dilate the new polygon by a scale factor of 0.8 with center of dilation at the center of the original polygon. 4. Rotate the new polygon clockwise until it is inscribed in the previous polygon. 5. Repeat the procedure on the new polygon.

3.3 Sample algorithm.

Given:	A circle with a vertical diameter.
Procedure:	1. Make a copy of the circle and its diameter to create a new circle with its corresponding diameter. 2. Dilate the new circle by a scale factor of 0.5. 3. Locate the new circle so that the lower endpoint of its diameter coincides with the upper endpoint of the diameter of the previous circle. 4. Repeat the procedure on the new circle.

3.4 Answers will vary. Sample response: The geometric sequence 10, 5, 2.5, 1.25, 0.625, … can be created by the following algorithm:

$$\begin{cases} g_1 = 10 \\ g_n = (0.5)g_{n-1} \end{cases}$$

* * * * *

***3.5** **a.** The length of the first side is 5 m; the length of the second side is 4 m.

b. Sample response: The robot will go forward and turn indefinitely.

c. Sample response:

- Spiral(x)
  - Forward(x)
  - Right(60°)
- Spiral($0.9x$)

3.6 **a.** The account balance after 1 year is $540.00; after 2 years, $583.20; after 3 years, $629.86.

b. Sample response: Yes, the algorithm is recursive because the same procedure is first used on initial information and then repeatedly used on previously generated information. The initial information is the initial investment of $500 and the annual interest rate of 8%. The previously generated information is the output from the machine, or the account balance. The process is the two steps in the function machine.

c. **1.** $2330.48

2. Since the initial investment was $500, the total interest earned is: $\$2330.48 - \$500.00 = \$1830.48$.

* * * * * * * * * *

Answers to Summary Assessment

1. **a.** Sample algorithm:

Given:	A square.
Procedure:	1. Make two copies of the figure. 2. Put one copy directly to the right of the original figure. 3. Put the other copy directly above the original figure. 4. The three figures now form a new figure. 5. Repeat the procedure on the new figure.

b. The following flowchart illustrates the algorithm given in Part **a.**

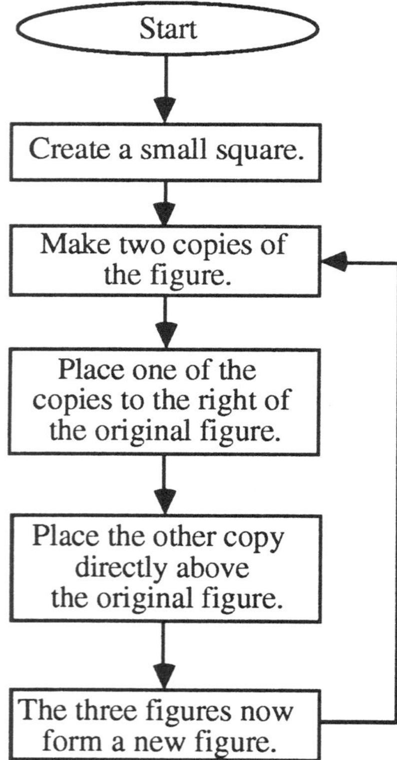

c. Sample response: Yes, the algorithm is recursive because the same procedure is first used on given information and then used repeatedly on previously generated information.

d. The next figure in the sequence is shown below:

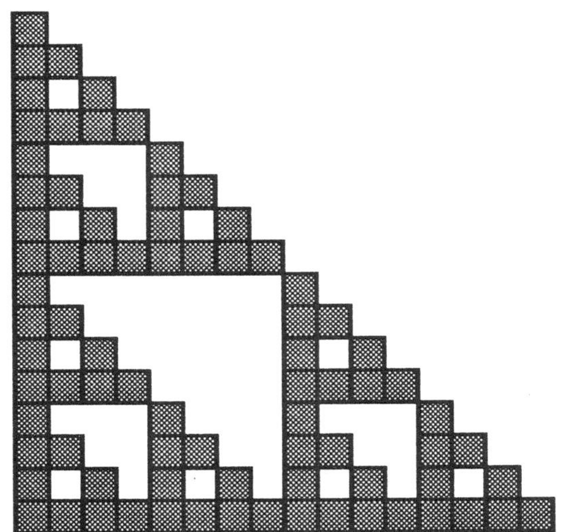

2. **a.** Answers will vary. Sample response:

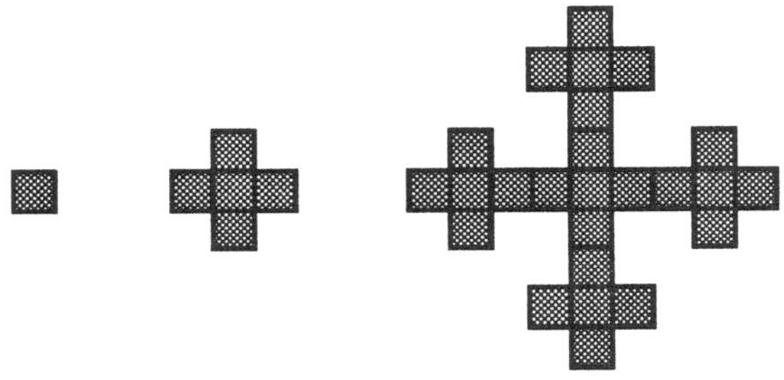

b. The following table describes an algorithm that could be used to create the sequence of figures given in Part **a**.

Given:	A square.
Procedure:	1. Make four copies of the figure. 2. Put one copy directly to the right of the original figure. 3. Put one copy directly to the left of the original figure. 4. Put one copy directly below the original figure. 5. Put one copy directly above the original figure. 6. The five figures now form a new figure. 7. Repeat the procedure on the new figure.

Module Assessment

1. Write an algorithm for inscribing a square in a circle, as shown below.

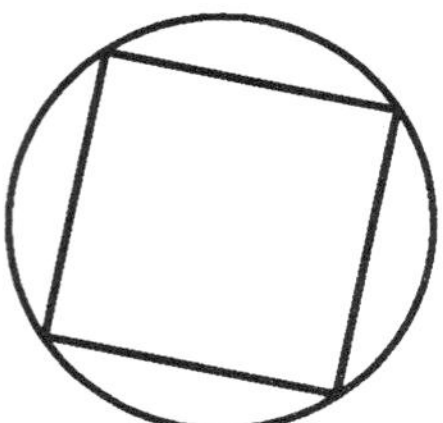

2. The following algorithm can be used to calculate the sample standard deviation of a data set.

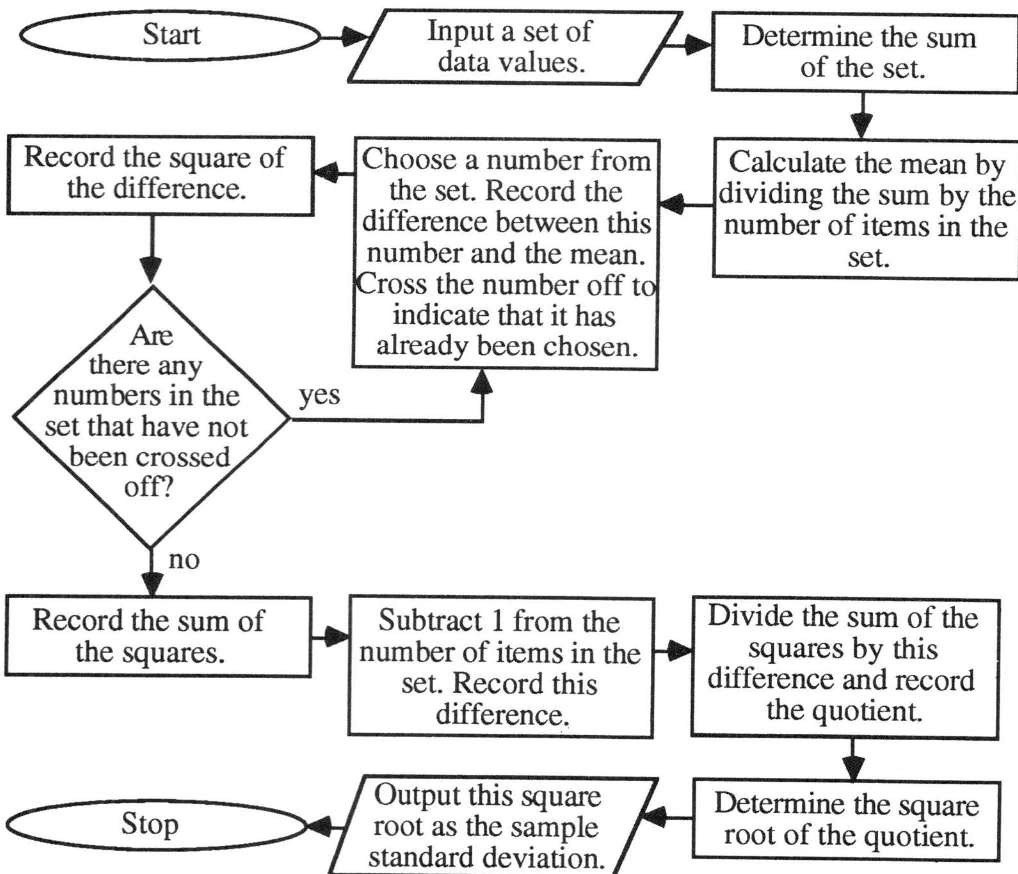

   a. Use the flowchart to calculate the sample standard deviation of the following set: {11, 13, 20, 25}.

   b. Use technology to confirm your response to Part **a**.

3. **a.** Create an algorithm for writing a fraction in lowest terms.

   b. Draw a flowchart for your algorithm in Part **a**.

Answers to Module Assessment

1. Sample response: Draw a circle, construct a point on the circumference, define the center of the circle as the center of rotation and transform the point using a rotation of 90°. Repeat this transformation twice using the image of the previous transformation as the preimage. Connect the four points consecutively to make a square.

2. **a.** Sample response: Input {11, 13, 20, 25}. The sum is 69 and the mean is 17.25. The differences are –6.25, –4.25, 2.75, and 7.75. The squares of the differences are 39.0625, 18.0625, 7.5625, and 60.0625. The sum of the squares is 124.75. Subtracting 1 from the number of items in the set yields a difference of 3. The quotient of the sum and this difference is $41.58\overline{3}$. The square root of the quotient is approximately 6.4. This is the sample standard deviation of the set.

   b. Technology will confirm that the sample standard deviation of this set is approximately 6.4.

3. **a.** Sample algorithm:

   1. Let a trial divisor of both the numerator and denominator be $d = 2$.
   2. Check to see if d divides evenly into both the numerator and denominator. If it does, divide it into both, and find the new denominator and numerator. If it does not, go to Step 4.
   3. Using the new numerator and denominator, go back to Step 1.
   4. Let d be 1 more than it was before.
   5. If d is more than half of the original denominator or more than half of the original numerator, you have checked far enough. The last denominator and numerator you found are the lowest terms of the original fraction.
   6. If d is still too small to fulfill the requirements of Step 5, go back to Step 2.

b. The following flowchart describes another possible algorithm for writing a fraction in lowest terms:

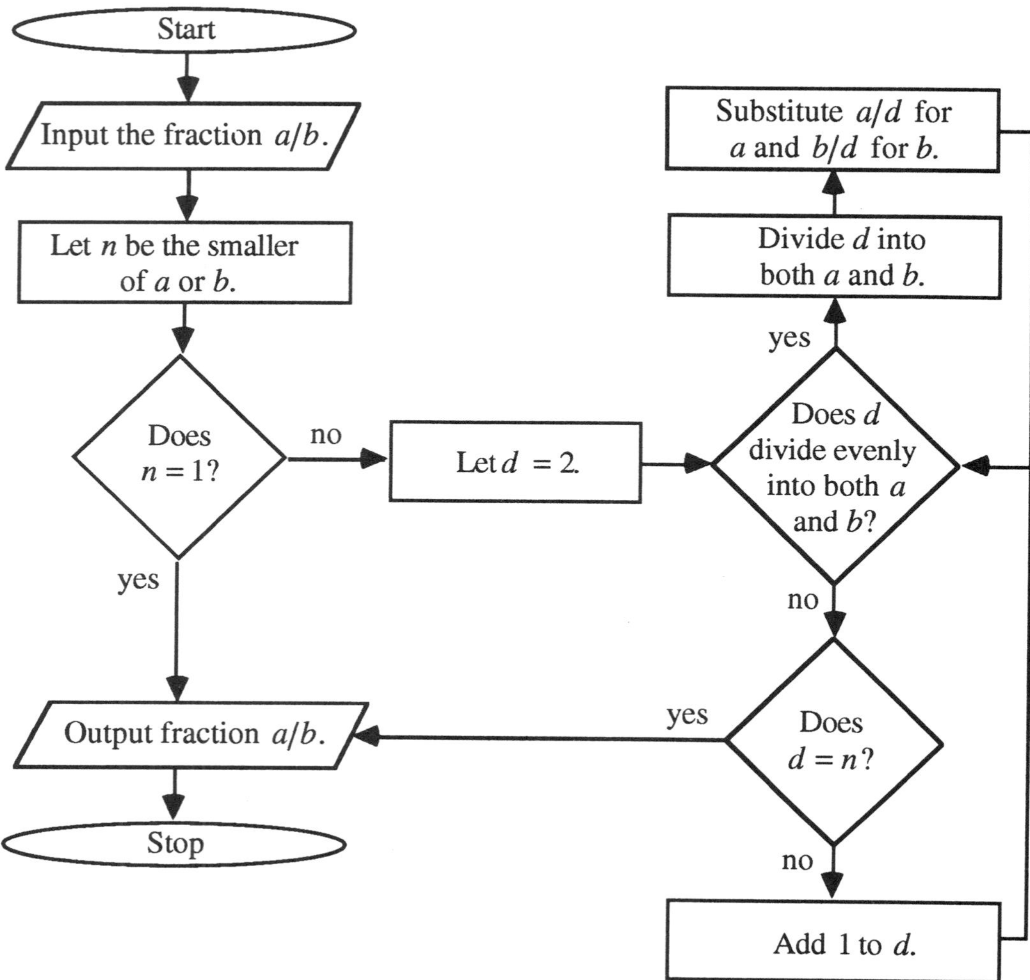

Note: Stopping d at $\sqrt{n}$ would make a more efficient algorithm. (Students must stop the divisors at some point, otherwise the algorithm will not terminate.)

Selected References

Coes, L., III. "Building Fractal Models with Manipulatives." *Mathematics Teacher* 86 (November 1993): 646–51.

Guy, R. *Fair Game.* Arlington, MA: Consortium for Mathematics and Its Applications (COMAP), 1989.

Graham, N. *Introduction to Computer Science.* St. Paul, MN: West Publishing Co., 1985.

Harel, D. *Algorithmics.* Workingham, England: Addison-Wesley, 1987.

Harel, D. *The Science of Computing.* Reading, MA: Addison-Wesley, 1989.

Kenney, M. J., and C. R. Hirsch, eds. *Discrete Mathematics Across the Curriculum K-12.* Reston, VA: National Council of Teachers of Mathematics (NCTM), 1991.

Kolman, B., and R. C. Busby. *Discrete Mathematical Structures for Computer Science.* Englewood Cliffs, NJ: Prentice-Hall, 1984.

Kraus, W. H. "Don't Give Up!" *Mathematics Teacher* 86 (February 1993): 111–12.

Merris, R. *Introduction to Computer Mathematics.* Rockville, MD: Computer Science Press, 1985.

Murril, P. W., and C. L. Smith. *Introduction to Computer Science.* New York: Intext Education Publishers, 1973.

Spencer, D. D. *Computers in Number Theory.* Rockville, MD: Computer Science Press, 1982.

Stiffarm, N. Unpublished set of recipes. Indian Studies Program. Harlem, MT. 1993.

Flashbacks

Activity 1

1.1 Find a rule that describes the following arithmetic sequence.

$$7, 21, 35, 49, 63, \ldots$$

1.2 Identify the quotient and remainder in each of the following divisions:

a. 37/25

b. 83/5

1.3 Given that $a = 1$, $b = -8$, and $c = 7$, use substitution to find the value of x in each of the following expressions.

a. $x = \dfrac{-b + \sqrt{b^2 - 4ac}}{2a}$

b. $x = \dfrac{-b - \sqrt{b^2 - 4ac}}{2a}$

Activity 2

2.1 Find the greatest common divisor of each of the following pairs of numbers:

a. 59 and 24

b. 42 and 66

2.2 Determine whether each of the following statements is true or false:

a. $\dfrac{16}{4} \leq \left(-2 + \dfrac{36}{6}\right)$

b. If x is 9, then $x + 1 < 10$.

2.3 A company pays its employees \$10 per hour, plus "time and a half" for overtime. Only those hours worked in excess of 40 hours per week qualify for overtime pay. Determine the weekly wage of an employee who works each of the following numbers of hours:

a. 30 hours

b. 50 hours

Activity 3

3.1 Write the first three terms of the sequence described by the following recursive formula:

$$\begin{cases} a_1 = 5 \\ a_n = 2 + a_{n-1},\ n > 1 \end{cases} \text{for } n > 1,$$

3.2 Consider the sequence 8, 14, 20, 26, … .

a. Write a recursive formula for the sequence.

b. Write an explicit formula for the sequence.

Answers to Flashbacks

Activity 1

1.1 Sample response: This sequence can be described by the explicit formula $a_n = 7 + 14(n-1)$.

1.2 **a.** quotient 1, remainder 12

b. quotient 16, remainder 3

1.3 **a.** $x = 7$

b. $x = 1$

Activity 2

2.1 **a.** 1

b. 6

2.2 **a.** true

b. false

2.3 **a.** \$300

b. \$550

Activity 3

3.1 5, 7, 9

3.2 **a.** Sample response:

$$\begin{cases} a_1 = 8 \\ a_n = 6 + a_{n-1}, \ n > 1 \end{cases}$$

b. $a_n = 8 + 6(n-1)$

Flowchart Template

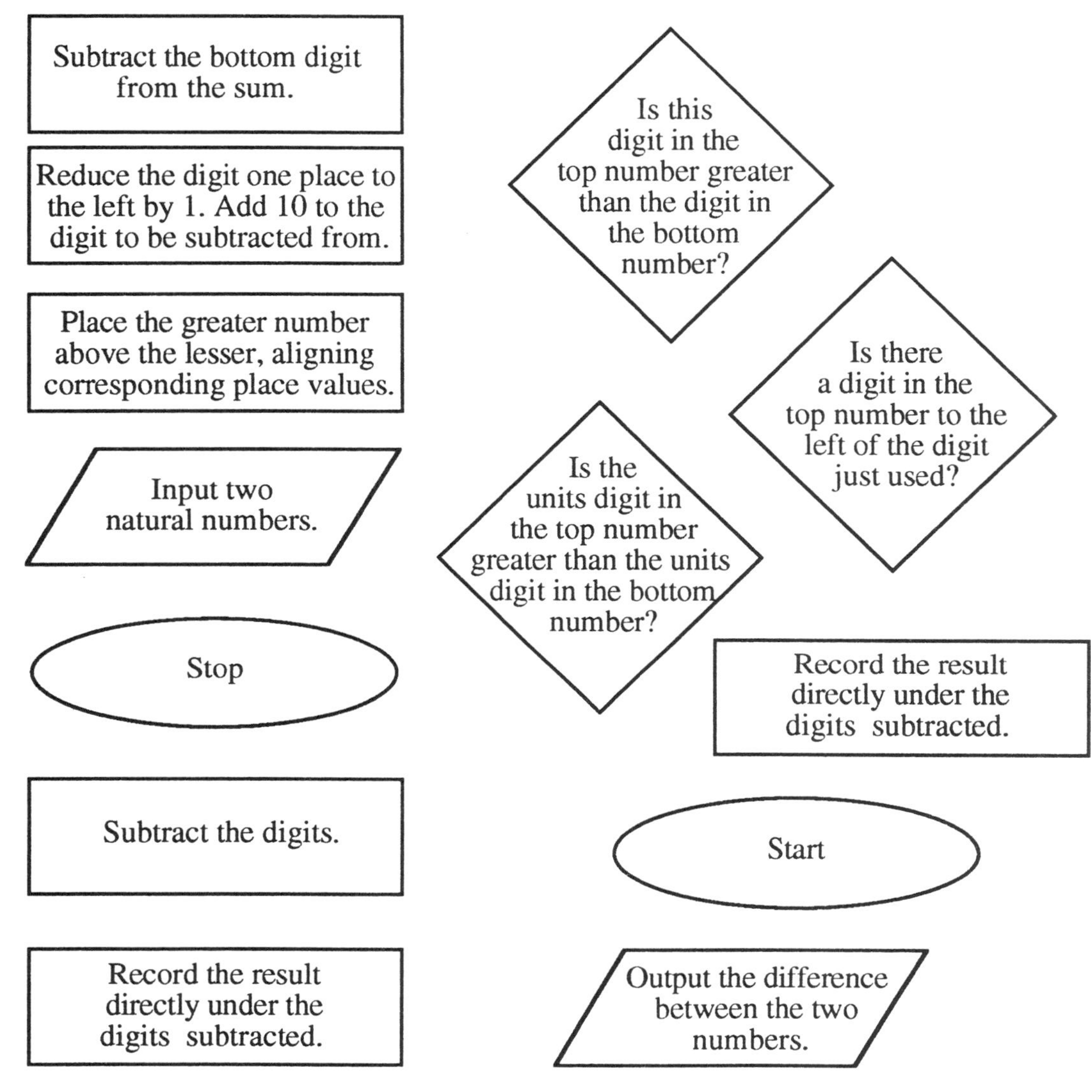